SALVA

RESCUED FROM THE DEEP
David L. Williams

LONDON

IAN ALLAN LTD

First published 1991

ISBN 0 7110 1963 0

Published by Ian Allan Ltd, Shepperton, Surrey; and printed by Ian Allan Printing at their works at Coombelands in Runnymede, England.

Contents

Introduction

Traditionally, salvage is perceived as the raising of sunken ships from the sea-bed or, more romantically, as diving operations on fabulous wrecks in search of treasure hoards from the Spanish Main or the Roman Empire. This popular imagery also, perhaps, includes the buccaneering exploits of rival tug crews vying to secure helpless ships whose plight is rated a poor second to their dogfighting to claim the prize.

Today, salvage means a great deal more. It also means a great deal that is more mundane, although, in a less dramatic manner, that is equally exciting and inspiring. The term "salvage" is used to describe a wide range of related activities associated with the recovery and restoration of lost or damaged property. The definition of the word, as given in the Oxford English Dictionary, illustrates this diversity:

'The saving of a ship or its cargo from loss by wreck or capture; the rescue of property from fire, wreckage or flood'

Lloyds Nautical Yearbook expands further on this description, concentrating on the word's origins in purely shipping and marine insurance terms:

'In maritime terms this relates to action carried out by a third party in the absence of a contract whereby property in peril at sea is saved. The term is often used to define the money paid to a salvor as a reward for such services but this should be termed a "salvage award". In marine insurance practice a salvage award, or part thereof, which is recoverable under a marine insurance policy is termed a "salvage charge". The term salvage may be used, in non-marine practice, to define property salved, as in the case of goods saved from a fire on land.'

In the context of maritime affairs, salvage still embraces the recovery by numerous means of all manner of vessels or commodities from the sea, but, increasingly often, objects having a special commercial, political or military value rather than just one of treasure trove. Salvage is now also concerned with the recovery of objects from other, quite different environments including that of outer space.

In the accounts in this book I have attempted to cover as many of these varied aspects of salvage as possible. Besides such topics as the largest vessels raised, the deepest operations, the biggest and most valuable hoards and so on, I have also described some of the less spectacular or newsworthy incidents in which salvage technology broke new ground or in which the salvors were confronted with pressures not

(above): Commemorative wall plaque at Ryde, Isle of Wight honouring the dead of the Royal George. The inscription reads, 'In memory of the many officers and men of the Royal Navy and Royal Marines who lost their lives when the Royal George sank at Spithead on the 29th August 1772 and who lie buried along this seafront; And here by friends unknown, unmarked, unwept, they rest'. D.L. Williams

(below): 'A real challenge' is how salvors described the double operation to salvage the Greek liner Navarino and the floating drydock in which she had come to grief. Neptun Roda Baloget

directly related to the recovery operation. There are also two chapters that concentrate on the restoration side of salvage.

Whatever the objective behind any particular salvage exercise, a common ingredient of all operations, to a greater or lesser degree, is the element of danger. Indeed, salvage is potentially one of the most dangerous activities that man engages in and although the rewards usually justify the risks involved, they are nevertheless hard earned.

The origins of salvage are lost in the mists of time but there are accounts in some of the earliest historical records that document efforts to rescue property, crops or other valuables lost or damaged in some disaster or other. This practice of saving from wastage any redeemable structure or commodity reveals salvage to be, from its earliest origins, one of man's more civilised pursuits. This apparent inclination to good husbandry of his resources which has continued to the present day is, perhaps, a good omen for man's future in a generation which is constantly reminded of the escalating depletion of so many of the planet's natural provisions.

In more recent history some notable examples of marine salvage have been chronicled for posterity, one of the most interesting being the unsuccessful bid to raise the wreck of the warship HMS *Royal George* which sank off Spithead on 29 August 1782. Rotten right through and a testament to the naval decline of her era, the *Royal George* capsized after her bottom virtually fell out during a careening operation known as a 'Parliament Heel', a manoeuvre which exposed alternate sides of her underwater hull for inspection and maintenance. More than 900 persons lost their lives when the ship went down.

Her wreck tested the ingenuity of contemporary salvors to the limit and some of the techniques employed laid the foundation stones of salvage methods which continued to have a practical value right up to our present, more technologically enlightened age. William Tracey, the first person to work on the *Royal George*, attempted to raise the wreck through the winter of 1783/1784 by a method in which the hull was secured to a salvage vessel and lift obtained progressively by the rising tide. The technique sounded ambitious but in fact was partially successful for Tracey managed to move the wreck some 25 metres during one attempt. Further efforts were thwarted, however, and Tracey was compelled to abandon the operation for reasons which have been the downfall of many a salvor for as long as salvage has taken place - bankruptcy and crippling disability resulting from the effects of prolonged deep diving.

William Tracey was followed by the brothers John and Charles Deane, who were the inventors of the first practical deep-sea diving helmet.

They worked on the wreck of the *Royal George* from 1836 to 1839 but were little more successful in their attempts although they did manage to recover a number of her cannons. The wreck was finally demolished where it lay in 1848 when it was blown up with explosives. Much of the

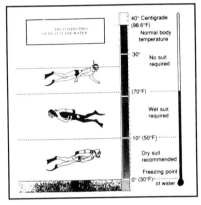

The physiological hazards that confront divers: (top): increasing water pressure. (below left): decreasing temperature. (below right): reducing colour and light level.

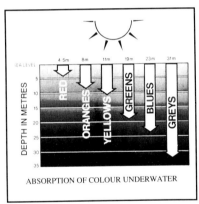

ship's scattered remains lie on the sea-bed off Spithead to this day.

The *Royal George* salvage operation is a particularly interesting one in that it, coincided, with the start of a period of tremendous progress in the development of both salvage technique and equipment. In those days much vital equipment, such as heavy lift gear and diving apparatus, was either unavailable to salvors or was severely restricted in its performance. Many marine salvage exercises, at that time, were still confined to operations conducted from the surface or, if underwater activities were possible, to little deeper than 20 metres (66 feet) in safety. Of course, the *Royal George*'s wreck lay in relatively shallow water - at low tide her masts projected above the surface. Nevertheless, working at these depths represented the frontiers of diving capability of the period, yet there were many other wrecks lying at significantly greater depths. Progress in

(above): Typical salvage scene - the cruiser HMS Gladiator, *which capsized in April 1908 following a collision, seen during the early stages of efforts to right her.* Roger Smith collection

Recovering the stranded and gutted L'Atlantique *(below): Tug crews pull in all directions as they compete to claim the prize.*
L.L. von Munching

INTRODUCTION

salvage practice from that point necessitated the development of equipment that would permit divers to work safely and with reasonable freedom well below the depths then possible.

Diving apparatus of various forms, both bells and suits, had been in use for centuries, as far back as the 4th century BC, but until the 19th century nothing had been designed that was both practical and reliable.

The modern history of the diving bell goes back to 1538 when Francis Bacon contrived a bell of sorts while, almost simultaneously, Leonardo da Vinci, pre-emptor of so many modern inventions, also prepared drawings for an underwater chamber. The first effective diving bell, invented by Sir Edmund Halley (of Halley's Comet fame), was introduced in 1690. While on the one hand, it was a practical device, on the other, it was severely limited in its application, representing the extent of development for open-based diving bells. It was not until Robert Davis produced his bell in 1917 that salvage companies had anything really suitable available for their work. Today, the world's largest diving bell, with a capacity of 8 cubic metres, is that of the Royal Navy's diving support vessel HMS *Challenger*.

The genealogy of the modern, tethered diving suit followed a similar pattern. In 1715, John Lethbridge designed a cylindrical diving dress which was constructed of wood with watertight arm holes. Strange though this contraption looked, it proved to be quite effective. Some seventy years later the next stage of development was reached when a man named Forfait developed a helmeted dress made of leather which was the first to enclose a diver from head to foot. Another step forward was made by a German, named Kleingert, in 1799. His one-piece outfit was described as the forerunner of the modern suit. It comprised a huge, egg-shaped helmet with jacket and breeches joined together by watertight connections.

The true precursors of the modern diving suit arrived in the early 19th century. The Deane brothers were the fathers of the modern diving suit having developed a watertight rubber diving dress with metal helmet by the early 1820s. The helmet, which was not attached to the suit, had glass face plates on three sides. Lead-soled boots, the first to be worn, completed the diving dress. The rights to the Deanes' design were acquired by Augustus Siebe, a German instrument maker, who set about incorporating improvements. His patented dress of 1837 was the first practical, safe diving suit and was more or less identical to the suits in use today. It consisted of a heavy metal helmet with breastplate, tough watertight diving dress, heavily weighted boots and a flexible tube carrying air pumped from the surface. Augustus Siebe founded the company of Siebe & Gorman which, in 1880, produced a lightweight version of the diving suit which permitted divers to work with greater independence.

For complete independence of operation, divers needed a self-

contained air supply. Work on autonomous breathing apparatus commenced in the early decades of the 19th century. By 1878, Henry Fleuss, an Englishman, had developed a self-contained oxygen lung and by 1900 the first compressed air breathing set had been designed. This was followed, in 1918, by the Ohgushi patented respirator. From this point a sequence of Frenchmen contributed to the development of efficient, lightweight and mass-producible self-contained breathing equipment - Yves Le Prieur, Maxime Forjot, Philippe Tailliez, and Georges Commeinhes. These efforts culminated in 1943 with the modern aqualung or self-contained underwater breathing apparatus (SCUBA) developed by Tailliez in conjunction with Jacques Yves Cousteau and Frederic Dumas.

This incorporated a demand regulator by another Frenchman, Emile Gagnan.

This brief account of the heredity of the diving bell and the diving dress has not been an irrelevant diversion. Marine salvage and diving are inextricably linked. To the modern underwater salvor this equipment is as vital as a spacesuit is to an astronaut or cosmonaut. Indeed, this analogy goes further for the deep-sea diver is often referred to as an aquanaut.

These developments had a profound impact on both diving and salvage capability. This is clearly revealed in the accelerated improvements to individual depth records that have followed the introduction of truly effective underwater apparel:

10

1895	A. Lambert (GB)	49.4 metres (162 ft.)
1896	Angel Erostarbe	56.7 metres (186 ft.)
1906	Royal Navy divers	64.0 metres (210 ft.)
1915	U.S. Navy divers	92.7 metres (304 ft.)
1937	M.G. Nohl (USA)	128.0 metres (420 ft.)
1945	A. Zetterstrom	161.0 metres (528 ft.)
1956	Lt.Cdr George Wookey (GB)	182.9 metres (600 ft.)
1961	Hannes Keller (Switz.)/ Kenneth MacLeish (USA)	222.0 metres (728 ft.)
1968	U.S. Navy aquanauts	312.5 metres (1,025 ft.)
1982	French divers	501.0 metres (1,643 ft.)

Note: simulated dives have now taken the depth records beyond 609.7 metres (2,000 ft.).

The development of underwater diving dress also focused attention on other, physiological impediments to working at depth. Divers have to breathe air under pressure in order to equalise the pressure in their lungs with the pressure of the surrounding water, pressure that increases the

INTRODUCTION

Long distance ocean towage forms a major element of the salvage companies' work load. One of the most famous tows of recent times involved the return of the Brunel-built iron screw steamship Great Britain *to Bristol from the Falkland Islands:*

(above) *The* Great Britain *positioned high and dry aboard the Ulrich submersible pontoon barge* Mulus III *en route to Port Stanley prior to crossing the Atlantic Ocean. The barge is under tow of the tug* Varius III *assisted by other small units.* Associated Press

(below) *The arrival at Avonmouth on 23 June 1970 at the end of the record-breaking 9,000 miles tow from the Falkland Islands.* Associated Press

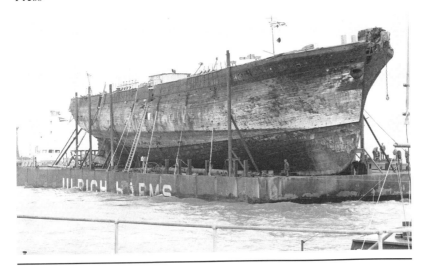

deeper they descend. On the surface and down to a depth of approximately 10 metres (33 feet), water pressure is equivalent to atmospheric pressure, i.e. 1.03 kg/sq.cm (14.7 lb/sq.in). At each additional 10 metres of depth the water pressure increases by one atmosphere and a diver's air supply must be compressed accordingly, otherwise his body would be crushed. The problem is that when air is compressed, nitrogen, which constitutes some 80% of the volume, is absorbed into the blood and other tissue fluids where it becomes highly concentrated. If a diver rises to the surface too quickly, the dissolved nitrogen is not expelled through the lungs in the normal way. Instead, it turns back into a gas within the body system interfering with the proper circulation of the blood. The condition that results is called the 'Bends'. Otherwise known as 'Compressed Air Sickness 'or' Divers Palsy it can be fatal in extreme cases. Even in less severe cases, intense cramp-like pain can be experienced in the limbs or body. The effects of the 'Bends' and working under pressure generally are cumulative and, over a long period, can lead to defective vision, crippling and irreversible damage to joints and muscle tissue, as well as total and permanent paralysis of the legs.

Apart from the potentially hazardous effects of incorrect decompression, the diver is also faced with numerous other physiological dangers. In the event of being brought to the surface at an extremely fast rate of ascent, the drastic pressure changes may cause bleeding from the eyes, nose, ears and mouth, burst lung (pulmonary barotrauma), embolism and other related physical and neurological conditions.

As if the dangers already identified are not sufficient in themselves for the deep-sea diver to contend with, he may also be vulnerable to toxicity from oxygen, carbon dioxide and carbon monoxide. Protection from all these risks depends on strict adherence to safe diving techniques, thorough and adequate training and, specifically, to constant, close attention to gas proportions and respiratory behaviour.

To ameliorate the dangerous side-effects associated with pressure changes, diving operations are strictly controlled both with regard to duration and exposure to compressed air breathing and in the process of return to the surface. A number of techniques are employed to reduce the risk of the 'Bends', the simplest of which is the use of the shot-line which extends down to the working depth and is marked at different levels. Divers suspend themselves on the line at decreasing depths for given lengths of time to allow the gradual re-adjustment to atmospheric pressure. This process is time-consuming, restricting the diver's effective working time during a dive, and is inappropriate in circumstances of injury, fatigue or hypothermia.

The inconvenience of this process for re-adjusting the pressure of divers' air supplies, particularly in commercial diving, led to the development of the submarine decompression or recompression chamber. In this, the rate of re-adjustment is precisely controlled by mechanical

INTRODUCTION

means while permitting the diver a degree of comfort during the re-acclimatisation process. The same apparatus is also employed, on the surface, for the treatment of divers suffering from the 'Bends' when emergency ascents have been necessary or when other uncontrolled ascents have occurred. In these circumstances the affected diver is placed inside the chamber and the air pressure increased to the level at which he was working underwater. It is then gradually lowered to normal atmospheric pressure at a controlled rate.

An alternative to normal diving practice, much employed by professionals, which provides the opportunity to extend significantly the period in which a diver can remain submerged, is the saturation diving technique. Pre-exposure for 24 hours to nitrogen-free artificial air, such as a mixture of oxygen and helium under pressure, causes the diver to become 'saturated' at that pressure and permits him to remain under pressure for much longer periods although routine decompression will be necessary when he ultimately returns to the surface. It is commonplace for professional divers to revert to a mixture of oxygen and helium, rather than normal compressed air, when working at depths greater than 40 to 50 metres (131.6 to 164.5 ft.). This is because at these pressures the dissolved nitrogen in compressed air causes confusion and narcosis. Unfortunately, however, the oxygen and helium mixture causes rapid loss of body heat, an equally serious hazard when working in cold water.

This somewhat lengthy diversion into the techniques of diving will, I hope, assist the reader to appreciate better the difficulties and dangers that confront those who undertake salvage operations in this alien environment. These physical dangers are not confined, either, to just those of a physiological, health-impairment nature. Light does not penetrate to very great depths so that divers often work in total darkness, particularly when within sunken hulls. Also, they are exposed to the ever-present risks of entrapment in a wreck or the severing of air supply lines and, in certain sea areas, the very real danger of attack by predatory creatures.

Whereas the physical challenges outlined above affect all divers, whether engaged in recreational, scientific or commercial activities, there are numerous other problems and issues that confront salvage organisations which can complicate recovery operations or which can exert indirect pressure on the salvage team. Indeed, the physical risks may even be increased as a result of these adjacent pressures when they make it necessary to achieve more rapid completion of the salvage. There are numerous examples of these indirect problems and, to some extent, I have selected the accounts that follow with these issues in mind.

For example, there was intense political pressure to achieve an expeditious removal of the wreck of the USS *Lafayette* whose capsized hull was a constant, embarassing and very public reminder of official blundering and incompetence. Equally, in the case of the Indian Airline's

13

747, the urgent need to recover the black box flight recorder can be understood for it was felt at the time that it alone could confirm the suspicions of sabotage to the aircraft.

Salvage operations can also be subjected to pressure from military authorities, either due to operations taking place in sensitive sea areas or as a result of security issues. The latter was certainly a paramount consideration in the operations to recover the U.S. Navy's Tomcat fighter lost off Scapa Flow and the nuclear bomb inadvertently dropped in the sea off the coast of Spain. And the advantages to the United States Government of getting hold of the

Russian 'Golf' class submarine which sank in the Pacific in the early 1970's requires no further explanation!

When ships have sunk with great loss of life, any salvage operation that follows has to be handled with extreme sensitivity. In the cases of the capsized ferry *Herald of Free Enterprise* and the Piper Alpha oil rig, when there was uncertainty as to who was or was not among the dead, a matter which exacerbated the already acute anguish of the relatives, it became a paramount objective to recover bodies as swiftly as possible to expedite the process of identification. These delicate operations, fraught with enough physical danger, were carried out, move by move, under the closest scrutiny by the world's news media due to the intense public interest in these disasters.

Another form of emotional pressure to which salvage operations are prone concerns the status afforded to certain wrecks when it has been impossible to recover the bodies of victims. The *Titanic* is perhaps the best known example of a wreck which has been designated as a grave. Another is HMS *Edinburgh*, the Royal Navy cruiser sunk off Murmansk in World War 2. It does not require much imagination to understand the concern of living relatives at the prospect of their loved-ones' final resting place being disturbed for what, on the face of it, is no more reason than financial gain.

A similar conflict of interests exists between archaeologists, concerned with the scientific recovery of artefacts from ancient wrecks and underwater sites, irrespective of their material value, and treasure hunters whose sole interest is perceived to be the retrieval of only the precious and financially valuable articles from these sources.

In this age of offshore exploration and supertankers, environmental pollution has become yet another major issue of concern to salvage organisations, a matter highlighted by a succession of disastrous accidents. Salvors have responded positively and effectively to these new threats, developing suitable techniques and equipment to deal with oil and chemical spills with the degree of urgency that these calamities demand. In the new International Maritime Organisation (IMO) Salvage Convention, provision has been made for a successful salvor to be entitled to enhanced reward as payment for any skills or effort made in preventing

INTRODUCTION

(above) *Another form of long distance conveyance. The damaged destoyer HMS* Southampton *on the deck of the large self-propelled submersible barge* Mighty Servant I *owned by Wijsmuller.*

or minimising damage to the environment. It also provides for special compensation to be paid to salvors, in the event of failure to salve a vessel or her cargo, where these represent a risk of damage to the environment and involve the salvor in executing procedures to control or prevent pollution. This is both timely and appropriate.

Finally, expanding on this point of commercial risk, the operations of salvage companies, and, in certain respects, marine archaeologists are especially vulnerable to financial pressures. Where commercial salvage business is concerned there is no other industry in the world which works in quite the same, precarious manner. International salvage is still usually undertaken in accordance with the 'No Cure - No Pay' principle of pure salvage, the exception being those instances where a specific danger of serious pollution exists. This means that, regardless of the time, effort and material expended by the salvor in his attempt to save a vessel or other salvageable commodity, if he is unsuccessful he receives no remuneration whatsoever. A standard form of contract covers this arrangement, the best known being the Lloyds Open Form agreement. Resulting from the new Salvage Convention, Lloyds has introduced a revised form which covers both types of situation.

The scientific fraternity, who invariably operate on a shoestring, are confronted with a similar problem in their efforts to recover what, to the public at large, may appear to be unglamorous and unimportant junk from

the sea-bed but which, to those intimately involved with the reconstruction of the past, are vital parts of the entire time jigsaw. Sponsorship provides the ideal solution for these projects but it is not that easy to secure when the finds are not sufficiently dramatic to make the newspaper headlines. Not every underwater excavation enjoys royal patronage or results in the sort of sensational salvage which was the culmination of the *Mary Rose* project.

Financial implications also have a profound influence on salvage operations for another reason. Some two hundred years after Tracey's attempt to raise the *Royal George* modern salvage technology stands at the very frontiers of science. The innovative high-tech engineering equipment required for the salvage and offshore operations of the late 20th century is comparable with that developed for the space exploration industry.

Specialised submersible search craft have been developed to permit the location of even the most minute items in the deepest waters. Sophisticated lifting apparatus has been created which is capable of raising the heaviest loads imaginable or of extricating material from the most inaccessible areas of the ocean floor. And the very latest scientific techniques are employed to preserve delicate treasures that would otherwise decompose when brought to the surface. All this demand on resources, both human and material, represents a considerable investment by the specialised salvage organisations, a commitment of assets which is difficult to justify when the return is so precarious. Yet without it, many salvage operations would be impossible to undertake and many more would end unsuccessfully. Big concerns such as Smit and Wijsmuller have experienced lean times during the current decade although marine accidents hit the news headlines often enough to give the impression that there are plenty of prizes there for the taking. The reality is that there are now, perhaps, too many companies chasing too few contracts with too little return. With so much capital tied up unprofitably in idle, expensive equipment and noprospect in sight of improvements to the salvage terms, rationalisation, retrenchment and bankruptcy constantly threaten.

Much of what has already been said regarding marine salvage appliesequally to salvage operations carried out in space, to recover lost or damaged satellites or effect repairs to orbiting vehicles. It goes without saying that in the airlessness of outer space the dangers that confront the space-walking astronaut are equally if not significantly more critical than those facing the aquanaut. Operational and development costs, too, are colossal but the burdensome expense of replacing lost equipment now makes it an attractive prospect for salvage recovery and the big insurance companies are, apparently, more than willing to underwrite it to make salvage worthwhile.

The interests of marine salvage companies and others engaged in supporting salvage activities are represented by the International Salvage

INTRODUCTION

Union based in London. Salvage practice is largely regulated by the provisions of the Convention of the Law of the Sea, an international agreement concluded under the auspices of the International Maritime Organisation. There is also a legal dimension to commercial salvage reflected in this and other internationally agreed conventions.

In the United Kingdom the Merchant Shipping Act (1894), part 9, the Civil Aviation Act (1949) and the Larceny Act (1916) are the relevant statutes exercising control over the execution of salvage work and the disposal of salved property. Objects which constitute a wreckor wrecked material are, even when in pices on the sea-bed, theproperty of their lawful owner. The law requires that any such property that has been recovered. Other than by salvage agreement or with the express permission of the owner, must be deposited with a Department of Transport appointed Receiver of Wrecks who will arrange for its disposal. If unclaimed after a year, the salvage articles become Crown property and are sold to raise revenue. It is a criminal offence to thieve from wreck or to fail to comply with the relevant statutes. Fines up to £100 can be imposed and offenders risk imprisonment for up to 14 years.

Similarly, with regard to ancient underwater sites, there are strict laws governing the exploration for and retrieval of artefacts. The Department of Trade can designate any site inside the United Kingdom's three-mile limit as being of special scientific interest and give it automatic protection under English law, in these circumstances by the Protection of Wrecks Act (1973). It insists on archaeologists being present at all times when wrecks are being explored.

Military wrecks are further safeguarded by the Protection of Military Remains Act (1896) which permits divers to visit or examine a site but which makes it an offence to tamper with, damage, move or remove any part of "a protected place" as it is designated.

Likewise, similar arrangements apply in most other countries. These laws reinforce the protection of crucial wreck locations from indiscriminate plundering, permitting their systematic exploration by professional experts whose primary concern is not monetary gain but the investigation of historic cultures.

In this introduction I have attempted to paint a general picture, in broad brush strokes, of the many aspects and facets of salvage. I have also made reference to the relevant legal issues and I have touched upon some of the technical complexities that have a bearing on salvage activities. It is not intended, however, that this book should be a dissertation on salvage technology or law, or for that matter, any of the other technically complex salvage subjects that would interest the professional. Instead, it is intended primarily to give the general reader an overview of salvage practice, illustrated by a number of different accounts of salvage experiences or methods. To underline this approach I am not an authority on salvage, nor do I have any particular experience or

knowledge that qualifies me to write on this subject. Rather, I have an amateur's keen interest in salvage affairs and a fascination for these epic operations and their unsung heroes. In each story I have attempted to convey something of the true life drama as these operations unfolded.

For those who may feel that some personal experience or involvement is essential to write with credibility on such a specialised subject, my credentials are suitably augmented by my participation, albeit on the fringes, in a minor salvage exercise.

Throughout my summer vacations while attending college in the 1960's I worked in a temporary capacity aboard the Trinity House lighthouse tender *Winston Churchill* whose area of operations extended along the Channel coast from Dungeness, Kent in the east to Portland Bill, Dorset in the west. To the south it extended to the Channel Islands.

During one of the *Winston Churchill*'s routine voyages, to service the *Royal Sovereign* and *Owers* light vessels, a violent spell of weather developed such as is not untypical at that time of year, as the Fastnet Race disaster in 1979 testifies. At the height of the storm, May Day distress calls were picked up from the German ketch *Monsun II* which was in difficulty off the Sussex coast, some 12 miles south of Selsey Bill.

In pitch darkness and quite appalling weather, the ship steamed hard to the yacht's rescue throughout the night but by daybreak the Monson II had already been abandoned and her occupants rescued by helicopter. Nevertheless, the *Winston Churchill* located the derelict and took it in tow to Littlehampton, as a consequence of which the ship's master was entitled to claim salvage. My minimal involvement in this operation, largely confined to observing the proceedings and supplying refreshments to those on the bridge who were really involved, earned me the princely sum of £5, my share of the prize.

The cheque was forwarded to me at college some time after the event, relieving, as I recall, one of numerous spells of serious financial embarassment that seem to be a feature of student life.

I trust that this book will prove to be an enjoyable read about a truly fascinating subject.

(right): The German ketch Monsun II, *abandoned in a storm, is recovered and taken in tow by the ship's launch from the THV* Winston Churchill. D.L. Williams

18

CHAPTER 1

Treasure From The Deep

Before 1981 the greatest depth at which divers had recovered cargo from a sunken wreck was 123 metres (440 ft.) when some £2.25 million worth of gold was brought to the surface from the passenger liner Niagara which was mined in 1940 off Bream Head, Whangarei, New Zealand.

Between 17 September and 7 October 1981 and later, between 2 and 11 September 1986, this record was comprehensively beaten, as was the record for the most valuable haul ever recovered. During these periods a team from Wharton Williams (2W) Underwater Engineering Contractors, based in Aberdeen, Scotland, recovered a fortune of gold bullion from the cruiser HMS *Edinburgh* which had been sunk in the Barents Sea, north east of Norway, in 1942.

The story began in April of that year when the Edinburgh was engaged to convey gold from the Soviet Union to the United Kingdom in payment for armaments supplied by the Allies during World War 2. At the time of the subsequent salvage, the gold, in the form of 465 ingots, was valued at approximately £44 million.

HMS *Edinburgh*, sister-ship to HMS *Belfast*, now permanently moored on the River Thames, sailed from Murmansk, on the Kola inlet, on 28 April 1942 loaded with her precious cargo, in company with the British destroyers *Foresight* and *Forester* and two Russian escort vessels. The group were covering the convoy QP11. On 30 April, when some 290 kilometres (180 miles) north of Murmansk, the group of ships was attacked by German submarines, a successful torpedo strike by U456 disabling HMS *Edinburgh*. The crippled cruiser was taken in tow but, with her steering gear quite useless and hampered by heavy seas, progress was slow. Under cover of squally snow showers, the enemy submarines, now joined by three destroyers, pressed home further attacks.

During the morning of 2 May near Bear Island (Bjornoya), while defending the helpless cruiser, a brief but fierce engagement took place between the Allied and German destroyers. This resulted in the attackers being driven off but not before one of the enemy destroyers had released a salvo of torpedoes, scoring further hits on the *Edinburgh*. There was considerable loss of life and the survivors were taken off the badly damaged ship which was expected to sink. But in spite of her severely weakened condition she continued to float though, in spite of her severely weakened condition. So, because there was a risk that her cargo of gold might fall into German hands if she was abandoned, the escorting

20

(top): HMS Edinburgh, built 1939, one of a pair of 8 inch-gun cruisers, the other, *HMS* Belfast, now a permanent floating museum moored on the River Thames. Imperial War Museum.

(above): HMS Edinburgh *sinking in the Barents Sea on 2 May 1942, her cargo of gold bullion destined to lie in a watery grave for almost 40 years.* Imperial War Museum.

destroyers were ordered to sink her by shell fire.

The bodies of the 57 casualties, 2 officers and 55 ratings, went down with the ship which was subsequently designated an official war grave for this reason. No attempt was made to salvage the gold immediately after the end of the war, partly through reasons of the limitations of diving equipment and experience but also because relations between the Soviet Union and the United Kingdom had soured, and the wreck, along with its priceless cargo, was apparently completely forgotten for the next thirty years.

Then, in the early 1970s, Keith Jessop of Jessop Marine Recoveries Limited, himself a diver and salvage expert, first heard about the loss of HMS *Edinburgh*. The curiosity triggered by this initial encounter soon developed into an interest of major proportions and, following detailed investigation into the ship's fateful, final voyage, he determined to set about the recovery of the bounty which he believed to be still secured within the ship's midships magazine into which it had been loaded some thirty years earlier.

There were a number of fundamental issues that had to be addressed before a serious attempt to fulfil this goal could be initiated.

First and, perhaps, foremost, neither the Soviet nor British authorities would or could indicate authoritatively whether the gold had been left aboard HMS *Edinburgh*. It was understood from all the contemporary evidence that there had been insufficient time for its removal from the ship but there was a very real possibility that an expensive salvage operation could be launched only to discover that the vaults were empty.

Second, even if the gold had gone down with the ship, as suspected, it was possible that, if the gold store had been ruptured during the attack, the ingots were scattered over the surrounding sea bed, buried by silt.

Last, but most certainly not least, the exact location of the wreck was unknown. Indeed, even the depth of the water in which it was lying was not certain, although it was believed to be a least 250 metres (820 feet) down, at a greater depth than had ever previously been dived in commercially.

All in all, such a venture presented enormous technical challenges so that, for anyone who could be persuaded to invest in it in the first place, financial involvement had to be regarded as nothing short of a very precarious gamble. Whereas success would guarantee them a fortune, this outcome was far from certain. Besides these matters, there was also the question of interference with a war grave to be considered.

During 1978, Keith Jessop made his first bid to locate the wreck of the *Edinburgh* but this was unsuccessful. In 1979 he joined forces with Wharton Williams, the leading underwater engineering contractors, as a result of which a full blown salvage operation was conceived. Two further years passed, during which the consortium finalised the project

plans, before the diving support vessel *Stephaniturm* finally sailed for the Barents Sea in the summer of 1981 for work to commence.

Among the problems that had to be resolved was clearance to work on the site of an official war grave. Even if the Admiralty could be persuaded to sanction an expedition by the 2W team, the relatives of the victims of the sinking might object to disturbance of the site, especially when the only motive for it was financial gain.

This issue, of interference with wrecks that contain the last remains of persons who lost their lives when the vessels sank, in order to remove valuable material property, is a controversial subject which arouses passions whenever it is raised. Even the salvage fraternity have divided opinions about the morality of such intrusion into what are regarded as sacred places of burial.

In the case of the *Titanic,* such was the concern of Dr. Robert Ballard, of the Woods Hole Oceanographic Institute, Massachusetts, that her site should be totally respected, that he insisted on any material lifted from the wreck, no matter how inconsequential, being dropped back into the sea. This included a small length of electric cable that was tangled around part of the submersible *Yankee* and inadvertently raised to the surface. These attitudes brought Dr. Ballard into direct conflict with his French counterparts, who were also engaged in the operation to locate and survey this most intriguing of wrecks. The French contingent did not regard the recovery and commercial disposal of artefacts from the *Titanic* as 'grave-robbing' and were determined to proceed with this activity regardless.

Ultimately, an irrevocable split between the two factions resulted. Dr. Ballard returned to the USA where he redirected his attention to the wreck of the German battleship *Bismark* but, as much through his campaign to impose appropriate respect, as he saw it, for the *Titanic* site as to anything else, the United States Government designated the wreck as inviolable under their law. Effectively this denied American salvors from deriving financial gain from this potentially lucrative source. Equally, it imposed restrictions on the sale or purchase of artefacts in the United States or any other transaction involving material recovered from the ship. But it did absolutely nothing to preclude such activities being conducted by foreigners outside their jurisdiction.

The French proceeded with their intentions, lifting the *Titanic's* safe to the surface and making a TV spectacular of opening it publicly in the Paris Museum of Science on 29 October 1987, ironically, at 4am so as to coincide with American prime viewing time. In the event, the whole show proved to be something of an anti-climax when the anticipated revelation of a missing, jewel-encrusted and highly ornamented copy of the Rubaiyat of Omar Khayam did not materialise. Subsequently, however, the French salvage company, Taurus International, has continued to collect artefacts from the *Titanic* deploying the small

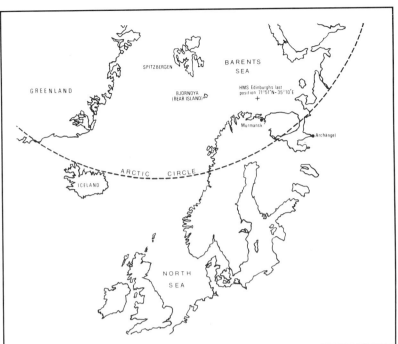

23

(above): Map of the Barents Sea, showing where HMS Edinburgh *sank.*

(left): A treasure of a different kind. A view showing the wide range and vast extent of the porcelain salvaged from the Dutch East Indiaman Geldermalsen. *It was auctioned by Christies in Rotterdam. The beauty of the chinaware had been well preserved by the gentle protection of the tea in which it had been packed for the voyage to Europe.* Christies

submarine *Nautile* from the support vessel *Nadir*.

It should be stressed, though, that the actions of the French outfit do not necessarily amount to desecration of an ocean grave. It all rather depends on your point of view for there was nothing to suggest that the French salvors had acted with impropriety or without displaying appropriate respect and deference in their search for relics or their disturbance of objects situated within the wreck. In the absence of internationally recognised and consistently imposed laws to regulate these matters, the argument will continue to rage.

Intimately concerned with this issue and mindful of the sensitivities of relatives at the prospect of the grave of their loved ones being disturbed, the 2W team concluded appropriate arrangements with the authorities in respect of the *Edinburgh*, ensuring minimum impact to the site and providing for memorial services to be conducted at the scene to emphasise the wreck's status as a place of rest. By careful research and pre-planning, the team anticipated that their incursions into the hull would be confined to the region in which the ammunition store was located which was remote from the accommodation and working areas of the ship. A permanent film record of the entire wreck site was also to be created for the naval authorities at the salvors' expense.

Negotiations also took place to conclude an agreement on the share out of the bullion between the salvors, the Soviet Government and the British Government, on the assumption that the salvage operation would be successful.

The *Stephaniturm* arrived at the search area on 17 September 1981, some four days after departing from Peterhead. She carried state-of-the-art navigation and position fixing equipment, sophisticated side scan sonar, a full saturation diving facility complete with diving bell and a SCORPIO (Submersible Craft for Ocean Repair, Positioning, Inspection and Observation) remotely operated submersible. Also on board were representatives of the Soviet and British Governments who were there to ensure that the operation was conducted in strict accordance with the terms and conditions of the salvage agreement.

Only a matter of days after arriving, the cruiser's wreck had been successfully located and positively identified. The ship was discovered lying in 244.6 metres (830 feet), still largely intact. The target area, from which access to the interior of the vessel would be gained, was pinpointed and surveyed by the SCORPIO which had been deployed as preparations for the commencement of the recovery operation got underway.

The saturation diving team was organised into rotas and their equipment established both underwater and aboard the Stephaniturm. The team comprised twelve divers, diving in pairs, who undertook a range of tasks commencing with cutting through the ship's side plating to gain access to the inside. Next, they would be involved in clearing rubble and scattered ordnance, then, the searching out of the bullion chamber and,

finally, the manhandling and loading of the ingots into cages for lifting to the surface. The longest decompression time was 7 days, 10 hours and 27 minutes.

The gold itself, the prize that had brought this concentrated group of experts to this bleak and freezing area of the Arctic, was found on 17 September, diver John Rossier earning the distinction of being the first to actually touch it. From that initial discovery, surrounded by unimaginable exhilaration both above and below the surface, the recovery team went on to retrieve another 430 ingots, some ninety per cent of the original treasure weighing nearly 5,590 kilograms (5.5 tons). The total value of the salved gold was £39.9 million, an all-time record for the most valuable salvage haul.

Just as the salvage team had reached the peak of its success, it was forced to abandon the operation. With deteriorating weather, all work was reluctantly halted, even though it was known that more gold remained in the wreck, and equipment was stowed in readiness for the return voyage.

On 7 October 1981, just prior to departing, the service of remembrance was held in honour of the officers and men who were killed aboard HMS *Edinburgh*. A poignant silence fell over the lonely site, as the salvage team paid its respects, followed by the laying of wreaths in the water over the site.

After the service was over the *Stephaniturm* headed for Murmansk where the Soviet share of the gold,158 bars worth £14.6 million, was handed over. Subsequently, the vessel returned to Scotland to a heros' welcome.

The operation had made history. Described as "the most successful diving operation ever carried out", the divers had established new depth records for free diving and deserved all the publicity and acclaim they received. Certainly, from a publicity point of view, only the salvage of the so-called 'Nanking Cargo' of Chinese porcelain from the wreck of the 18th century Dutch East Indiaman *Geldermalsen* in 1985 rivalled the *Edinburgh* group's success. The fact that this vast hoard of incredibly well preserved porcelain was publicly auctioned by Christie's in Amsterdam no doubt had a great deal to do with this.

On arrival in the United Kingdom, the balance of the salvaged gold was distributed. The British Government received £7.3 million. The rest was shared out between the members of the salvage consortium, £1.8 million to Jessop Marine Recoveries Limited and £16.2 million to Wharton Williams Limited. Though Wharton Williams received the largest proportion of the prize, they had been obliged to fund the operation entirely from their own resources and at their own risk when it had proved impossible to attract other investors.

The salvage team was determined to return to the Barents Sea the following season to recover the remainder of the gold but, for a variety of reasons, these plans were not fulfilled and the second expedition was put off time after time. It was not until 1986 that, finally, these ambitions were realised and the scheduled and inevitable return took place.

On 29 August 1986, the diving support vessel *Deepwater II* left Aberdeen conveying more of 2W's specialist underwater engineering equipment, including new facilities developed since the previous expedition. There was the submarine surveillance craft RCV-225/HTC, equipped with high thrust motors and remote-controlled colour television camera, and the *Rigworker* R3000 robot submersible, each complete with its support team of ROV specialists.

Within hours of arriving over the wreck site, on 2 September, the RCV-225 submersible was lowered into the water and manoeuvred down to the sunken hull. Entering the cruiser's side through the hole cut by divers five years previously, the RCV surveyed the magazine in the vicinity of where the gold already recovered had been located, sending back to the surface video pictures to enable the recovery team to formulate its plan of action.

Meanwhile, the diving bell was being deployed in preparation for the first divers to commence work. Before the first day had ended divers were already working inside HMS *Edinburgh*, removing rubble and large amounts of ordnance that had occupied the steel bunker along with the bars of gold.

This in itself highlighted another hazard that confronts divers working on wartime wrecks such as HMS *Edinburgh*. Explosives that have lain around on the sea bed, slowly corroding for years are notoriously unstable and the risk of detonation has to be taken seriously at all times. The transfer of shells and other ammunition from within the magazine had to be executed with extreme care. At all times the robot submarine *Rigworker* was on hand to assist the divers in this work.

Early on 3 September, aided by light provided by one or other of the two robot submarines, the first of the residual ingots was unearthed. Over the ensuing nine days, 28 more were discovered, worth around £2.7 million. While this was an extremely valuable haul when measured by most other standards, it was achieved at a price of considerably more effort than had been necessary for the much greater haul recovered in 1981.

As a lasting monument to HMS *Edinburgh*, the full-site survey of her final resting place was now carried out for the Admiralty, prior to the winding up of the salvage exercise. This yielded a very special but totally unexpected treasure. This was the ship's bell which was found lodged on the canted deck of the main bridge structure. A diver was guided to the scene of the find where he ecstatically claimed the prize. Transferred to the ROV for a poignant return to the surface it was later displayed on the deck of *Deepwater II* along with some of the gold bars. Its name and date, "HMS *Edinburgh* - 1939", that had been inscribed in the bell when

it was cast, were still clearly evident.

Again, the gold bullion was divided-up according to the proportions agreed with the British and Soviet Governments prior to the first expedition. The Soviet share was transferred to a missile cruiser in the small hours of Saturday 13 September.

Later that same day, the salvage operation was formally terminated with another memorial service to the victims of the *Edinburgh* sinking. Immediately afterwards, the *Deepwater II* sailed from the scene, arriving at Peterhead on Thursday 18 September to a tumultuous welcome. In a ceremony the following day, the ship's bell recovered from the wreck was presented to Lt. Commander Ken Napier, master of the modern Type 42 destroyer *Edinburgh* on which it was to remain. No doubt the bell will be passed on to future Royal Navy vessels bearing the same name, as a lasting reminder of this World War 2 casualty and her unusual mission. It will, of course, also remain as a lasting tribute to the record-breaking salvage operation in the Barents Sea from which it was retrieved.

The balance of the 29 gold bars were now distributed, from which the salvage consortium derived £1.2 million. The two salvage expeditions had earnt them in total £19.2 million. Against this it had cost approximately £2.6 million to finance the venture. Almost from the start it had been established that Wharton Williams would have to fund the search and recovery operation if it was going to come to fruition, but, with no guarantee of a positive outcome, it was a not inconsiderable risk. The salvage team would no doubt argue that it was a calculated risk, even a sound investment for, through careful planning and the utilisation of professional skills and teamwork, it had earnt them a princely return.

(below): Presentation of the cruiser HMS Edinburgh's *bell by Mr. Larry Kelly to Lt. Commander Ken Napier, master of the Type 42 destroyer of the same name, on 19 September 1986. Also in the picture are the joint managing directors of the salvage company, Mr. Malcolm Williams (left) and Mr. Rick Wharton (right).* Aberdeen Journals

Phoenix from the Ashes

The marine insurance term "constructive total loss" is used to describe a severely damaged vessel for which the cost of reconstruction would exceed the value of the ship itself if restored to sound order. In these circumstances the usual course of action is to send the vessel in question, if still afloat, for scrap to obtain the maximum possible recompense for the hull underwriters. There are exceptions to this practice which occasionally arise when other, unusual factors dictate restoration regardless of cost. This was often the case during wartime when shipping losses were so severe and certain types of vessel in such short supply that there were benefits in returning otherwise irretrievable ships to service rather than further burden already overworked shipyards with new orders.

Two cases, where this degree of salvage restoration was undertaken, involved a pair of troopships, one American, the other British. This account concentrates on the actions to save the vessel, the USS *Wakefield* ex *Manhattan*, a former trans-Atlantic liner operated by the United States Lines before the war. She sustained extreme damage from an unexplained outbreak of fire during a westbound crossing of the Atlantic in September 1942. Her British counterpart, the Cunard White Star liner *Georgic*, with whom she had shared a friendly rivalry for cabin-class passengers during peacetime, was also gutted following an air attack, while unloading at Port Suez on 14 July 1941. The *Georgic*'s rather similar experiences will be briefly recounted at the end of the chapter.

On the afternoon of 3 September 1942 the USS *Wakefield* was one day out from New York, sailing in the eastbound convoy TA18, escorted by the cruiser USS *Brooklyn* and the destroyers USS *Mayo* and USS *Madison*, when a fire of undetermined cause broke out on B deck on her starboard side. Despite all efforts, the fire spread rapidly out of control and within a quarter of an hour had engulfed the decks immediately above and below the point of origin. Both the ship and her occupants were in dire peril, and, saving the passengers and then the vessel in that order of priority became issues of immediate and paramount importance.

At the time, the *Wakefield* was some 370 kilometres (200 nautical miles) from Halifax, Nova Scotia and approximately 650 kilometres (350 nautical miles) from Boston, Massachusetts, in seas known to be infested by enemy submarines. In spite of the risk of being torpedoed, the blazing ship was turned broadside into the wind so that the smoke was blown away from her to allow the escort vessels to come alongside and take off passengers. Flames had already devoured the ship's upper structure and could be seen clearly licking around the forward funnel. Time was of the

(top): The Wakefield (ex-Manhattan) *ablaze in the North Atlantic on 3 September 1942.* US Coast Guard

(above): Evacuation of the Wakefield, *a US cruiser in the foreground and a destroyer further along the transport's side.* US National Archives

essence but quick action by the accompanying ship meant that all aboard were safely evacuated without loss of life, leaving the *Wakefield* temporarily abandoned to her fate, drifting without power and burning out of control.

The ship's master, Commander Harold Gardner Bradbury, requested to be returned to the *Wakefield* with a fire-fighting party, a request that was duly granted. Unfortunately his bid to extinguish the fire was totally ineffective and it was soon necessary for the ship to be abandoned for a second time.

For four days afterwards, the fire raged unabated for there was little opportunity to arrest its progress. The prospects for the former liner looked bleak indeed and it was a miracle that she had not already sunk.

Meanwhile, in New York, where notice of the fire aboard the *Wakefield* had been brought to the attention of the United States Navy's Supervisor of Salvage, the initial response to the emergency was swiftly formulated. An impressive, smoothly professional and well co-ordinated salvage operation was set in motion, triggered by a string of key commands issued from the headquarters of the Chief of Staff, Eastern Sea Frontier.

America was desperately short of ocean-going troop transports so it was determined that however remote the chance of saving the *Wakefield*, all effort would be made and all assistance rendered in a bid to achieve this. In the first instance this meant that the vessel had to be secured and the fire, still raging on board, extinguished before the ship was damaged beyond recovery.

Two large salvage tugs, the *Foundation Franklin* and *Foundation Aranmore* were directed to the *Wakefield's* aid, sailing, respectively, from Halifax and Massachusetts Bay. Simultaneously, the salvage vessel *Relief* was despatched to the scene, while Captain Earl Palmer, a respected salvage and towage expert, was appointed to advise on the first, most critical stage of the operation - getting the ship safely to port where the fire could be fought more effectively.

As the salvage vessels were proceeding to the scene of the disaster, vast quantities of liquid fire-fighting foam were ordered to be transferred from Philadelphia to the Naval Air Station at Quonset Point, Rhode Island, for delivery to the *Wakefield*'s eventual destination, once determined. At the same time, detailed deck plans of the *Wakefield* were hurriedly obtained from her builders and large scale charts of all possible anchorages and harbours on the eastern seaboard of North America were made available to assist the operation controllers in preparing for the next phase of the exercise, assuming the *Wakefield* safely made landfall.

Analysing these charts revealed that McNab Cove, in the outer harbour at Halifax, was the best place to beach the *Wakefield*. Halifax was already the nearest port to the stricken ship but it also had readily available the kinds of equipment, manpower and other essential material

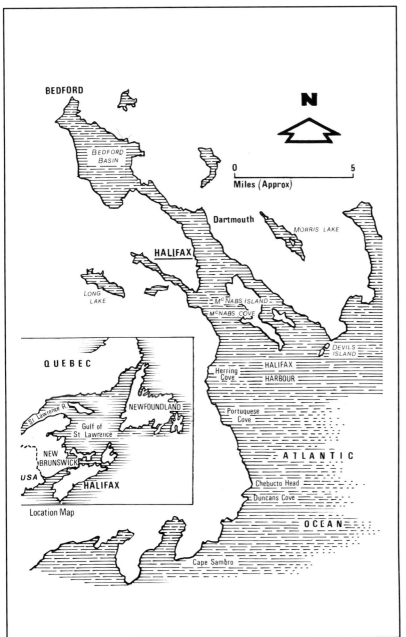

(above): Map of Halifax harbour showing McNab's Island and Herring Cove, outside the harbour defences, where the Wakefield *was temporarily anchored.*

32

(top): The Wakefield *after the fire had been extinguished, awaiting temporary repairs at Halifax.* Canadian Dept of National Defence

(above): Close-up of the ship, showing the detail of the fire damage. Canadian Dept of National Defence.

necessary for her recovery. As for McNab Cove, with its gently shelving sandy beach, it was ideal for stranding such a crippled vessel. It was readily accessible, within the immediate vicinity of the Royal Canadian Naval Dockyard, and provided ample room for small craft to manoeuvre around the transport while containment measures and preliminary repairs were being carried out. The only potential hazard was the Naval Fuelling Pier which stood close to the approach route to the beach.

In readiness for the arrival of the blazing transport, two 33.5metre (110foot) wooden barges were secured near the beaching point, each with a 15.25metre (50foot) high staging constructed upon it, from which, once alongside, firemen could fight the fire from a higher vantage point.

All the gear assembled at the Naval Air Station at Rhode Island was now moved to Halifax while Canadian Navy mechanics in the dockyard workshops were set to work fabricating adaptor couplings to permit Canadian and American pumps and hoses to be connected together. A large number of Canadian Navy ratings were also assembled to act, temporarily, as auxiliary fire-fighters.

Out at sea, the tugs had successfully attached lines to the *Wakefield* and the tow to Halifax was proceeding. The ship's plating, red-hot through the inferno raging within, was inclined to buckle inwards each time a tug nosed too close to the sides of the hull. The intense heat also threatened the integrity of the tow lines secured to the ship: these were constantly in danger of burning through. To prevent this, hoses sprayed sea water over them for the duration of the tow.

33

Hampered by strong westerly winds that both fanned the flames and made it difficult for the tugs to maintain the transport's heading, the tow finally arrived off Chebucto Head in the early hours of 8 September. Commander Bradbury and his team, who were once more aboard the *Wakefield*, had locked the rudder amidships to assist directional control of the ship. They had also flooded the main magazine and other ammunition stores.

This latter, routine action had particular significance in these circumstances, in order to quell any anxiety among the citizens of Halifax at the prospect of a major explosion within the harbour limits. In December 1917 such an eruption had occurred following a collision between the French vessel *Mont Blanc*, which had been carrying a cargo of high explosive, and the Norwegian steamship *Imo*. The magnitude of the explosion was such that the houses in the Halifax suburb of Richmond were virtually reduced to matchwood, as if struck by an earthquake. The official figures for casualties and damage were horrific - 3,500 dead or missing, 8,000 seriously injured, 3,000 properties totally destroyed and overall damage estimated at Canadian $30 million. Clearly the *Wakefield* was not carrying the quantities of explosive material that had been in the holds of the *Mont Blanc*, but memories of such a devastating experience take a long time to fade.

The *Wakefield* was slightly down at the stern but otherwise had no list, a testimony to the quality of her construction given the forces that had ravaged within her hull.

Owing to the strong prevailing winds and the fact that many of those aboard the flotilla of salvage craft were not familiar with the navigable channels leading into Halifax harbour, it was decided to wait until daytime before proceeding beyond the harbour defences for what was to be the most delicate phase of the tow. With the *Foundation Franklin* pulling from the bow, the *Wakefield* along with her small convoy of attendant craft was temporarily manoeuvred into Herring Cove and anchored there, a mile offshore.

At 14.30 hours local time on 8 September her anchor chain was burned through - it could not be hoisted by the windlass because of the loss of all generated power - to free her for the final move to the beachhead, through the opening in the harbour defences and into the outer harbour.

Once more, the *Foundation Franklin* took up the lead position, ahead of the *Wakefield*, assisted by a small harbour tug. Distributed around the transport were five other vessels. There was a harbour tug on either side on her forward quarters, navy tugs on each side on her stern quarters and the *Relief* secured to her stern.

Once into the harbour, the *Wakefield* was turned through almost 180 degrees and lined up with the beach at McNab Cove. After supplying sufficient forward momentum to drive her aground, the tugs dropped their lines and drew clear. All was going according to plan until a sudden, strong gust of wind swung the ship rather more to starboard than was desirable, causing her to strike the adjacent Naval Fuelling Pier, cutting into the pier structure though not, fortunately, the pipelines.

Somehow she was wrestled clear, eventually being stranded, with a slight list to port, at 17.40 hours, about an hour before high water. Her stern still floated at full tide so it was secured to a mooring buoy in order to keep her steady.

Fires were still burning fiercely in three holds and in the crew's quarters on two deck levels. Access to the fire through hatches 3, 4, 5 and 6 was best from the port side so the two dumb barges were positioned on this side of the ship. Other fire parties boarded the *Wakefield* to fight the fire from the promenade deck which could be safely accessed along its entire length.

Fire-fighting continued throughout the night of 8 September and for the next four days. Fresh outbreaks constantly frustrated progress while the weather conditions were far from sympathetic with high winds tending to fan the blaze and make it difficult for the firemen to concentrate the jets of water on the seat of the fire.

However, on 9 September the fire had been quelled to a sufficient degree that a party of ratings was permitted to board the vessel to

commence the clearance of débris, ash and other wreckage. At the same time, it was possible to conduct a preliminary survey to attempt to ascertain the extent of the damage to the critical fabric of the ship. This revealed that the main engines and boilers had not been affected and were completely intact, although the majority of the auxiliary plant was damaged beyond recovery. Much of the steelwork above the waterline, both plating and structural members, was badly buckled and seriously weakened. Nevertheless, the overall prognosis was fairly good and, although subsequently the *Wakefield* was declared to be a constructive total loss, surveyors and salvage experts were optimistic that she could be restored and that effort spent in preparing her for a voyage to a repair yard would most certainly not be wasted.

On 12 September, the fire aboard the *Wakefield* was finally extinguished, eleven days after it had broken out. Removal of débris was now accelerated as pumping-out of the large quantities of hose water was commenced. Two days later, at 10.15 hours, the *Wakefield* was refloated and transferred to Pier B, Halifax Docks where temporary repairs, prior to leaving for the Boston Navy Yard, were to be carried out.

Over the next two weeks the ship's weakened decks were shored up with wooden beams while other interior and exterior strengthening of the hull was carried out. Holes in her hull were patched over; transverse and longitudinal frames throughout the ship were reinforced. Simultaneously, basic cooking and sleeping facilities were brought aboard to provide bearable accommodation for the skeleton crew that would remain aboard the *Wakefield* for the tow to the United States.

While these preliminary repairs were in progress, the weather once more turned severely inclement, threatening to terminate the restoration of the *Wakefield* before it had begun. A torrential rainstorm, accompanied with storm force winds, looked ominously like flooding the ship, causing her to capsize at her berth, as water accumulated on her decks. Frantically, workmen cut additional scuppers in her sides on the upper deck levels to allow the rainwater to drain away and gradually, as the crisis passed, the seriously listing ship regained an even keel.

The tow to Boston commenced on 29 September, somewhat delayed by the extra work resulting from the adverse weather conditions. Under the charge of four tugs, it passed off without further incident.

Upon her arrival at Boston, the United States Government purchased the charred hulk that had once been the luxury liner *Manhattan* from her former owners, the United States Lines, for there was little prospect of her ever resuming her peacetime passenger carrying employment, even though all her fittings and furnishings had been removed prior to commissioning, with eventual restoration for this purpose in mind. The Government elected to have her rebuilt instead, virtually from the keel up, as a purpose-designed troop transport.

The reconstruction occupied the next sixteen months, from October

(top right): The White Star liner Georgic *prior to World War 2.* World Ship Photo Library.

(centre right): sunk at Suez following the German air raid. World Ship Photo Library.

(bottom right): and as rebuilt, seen once more in peacetime colours. World Ship Photo Library.

1942 to February 1944, as, Phoenix-like, a new *Wakefield* arose from the ashes and twisted metal. She was stripped almost to the waterline with new hull plates replacing the weakened and damaged patches along the walls of her hull. Top hamper was removed down to the main deck. When rebuilt it was without the promenade deck which had previously housed all her public rooms, confirming that her passenger liner days were definitely over.

Inside, all vestiges of the accommodation that had been originally provided for civilian passengers in small cabin units was dispensed with and in its place troop dormitories were constructed. Some areas, such as the former dining room were retained but all traces of passenger refinements were removed as the emphasis was switched to functionalism and robustness so that the demands of feeding huge numbers of troops in vast sittings could be met.

Externally, apart from the deletion of her promenade deck, the *Wakefield* did not look that drastically different. The majority of her surviving metal lifeboats were not re-installed but along each side of her superstructure were attached 38 large Carley life-rafts.

The *Wakefield* was recommissioned at Boston on 10 February 1944 with Captain R.L. Raney, United States Coast Guard, in command. Her first departure, on 13 April, launched a tour of duty which included twenty three Atlantic round trips, between Liverpool and Boston, and three crossings of the Pacific. She supported the Normandy landings and later the Allied thrust through Italy into Southern France with repeated calls at Taranto, Naples and Marseilles. Before the war's end she had carried a total of 217,237 troops.

There followed a brief spell of peacetime trooping duties as the *Wakefield* continued to repay the cost of her rebuilding, until on 15 June 1946 she was decommissioned and laid up in the reserve fleet, first in the Brooklyn Navy Yard and later in the River Hudson. Strangely she remained there, idle and wasted, until disposed of for scrap in May 1964.

The *Georgic's* similar, almost identical, experience to the *Wakefield* started when she was bombed and burnt out beyond recognition at Port Tewfik, Suez Canal on 14 July 1941.

Reclamation was also decided on in her case so, after being raised on 27 October that year, she proceeded on an incredible, long-distance voyage, for a ship in her condition, back to the United Kingdom for reconstruction by Harland & Wolff of Belfast, her builders.

After a measure of patching up, she left for Port Sudan on 29 December towed by the cargo vessels *Clan Campbell* and *City of Sydney*.

Arriving there thirteen days later, more temporary repairs were carried out in readiness for the next leg of the tow. This took the *Georgic* to Karachi, under tow of the cargo ships *Haresfield* and *Recorder* and the tugs *St Sampson* and *Pauline Moller*, where she arrived on 31 March 1942. During the tow, the *St Sampson* foundered in severe weather.

Again, further repairs were completed including, for the first time, attention to her engines. Another move took her to Bombay in December 1942 where more repair work was undertaken. Finally, on 20 January 1943, the *Georgic* headed back to Belfast under her own steam and unescorted for much of the journey home.

Liverpool was reached on 1 March 1943 from where, after a few days, she was transferred to drydock in Belfast. Immediately, workmen descended upon the battered vessel, stripping her down to the main deck level. As was the case with the *Wakefield*, the British Government purchased the *Georgic* from the Cunard White Star Line, her owners, signalling the termination of her civilian career. Also, like the *Wakefield*, she bore only a passing resemblance to her former self, as rebuilt. Her forward, dummy funnel and main mast were not restored. Internally her accommodation spaces were completely revamped for exclusive troop carrying operations although, after the end of the war, they were further adapted for the carriage of emigrant travellers in a single, rather austere class.

The *Georgic* re-entered service in December 1944, some three and a half years after being knocked-out by the Germans. She survived until February 1956, a slightly better post-war record than the *Wakefield*, but, like her American contemporary, the cost of her restoration had been fully repaid by the sterling service given during those final twelve years.

38

(above): The rebuilt Wakefield, after the war, being towed into the Erie Basin at Brookln, New York, proir to entering the Todd Shipyard. Although she has lost one deck she is not otherwise too much different externally. Steamship Historical Society of America

Ferry in Peril

On Friday 6 March 1987, shortly after leaving Zeebrugge Harbour, Belgium, on her evening sailing to Dover, the Townsend Thoresen, 7,951 gross registered tonnes cross-Channel passenger ferry *Herald of Free Enterprise* dramatically capsized and rolled over on to her port side less than a mile from port. She came to rest on her beam ends in what were, fortunately, fairly shallow waters, about half of her hull remaining exposed above the surface. Had she been in deeper water she would most probably have inverted totally. As it was 188 out of the 573 persons on board lost their lives. With such an horrific death toll it is almost irrelevant to contrast "bad" with "worse" but the fact is that, had the Herald of Free Enterprise turned over completely, probably everyone on board would have perished.

    The accident had occurred in an extremely short period of time, certainly no more than two minutes, adding to the shock of such a terrifying experience. In so brief a time it was not possible to send out a distress call or launch life saving equipment and, tragically, the survivors had to wait in the dark, freezing cold, half-submerged tomb while nearby vessels, that had witnessed the accident, informed the authorities who wasted no time in alerting the rescue services.

    On the face of it the *Herald of Free Enterprise* disaster seemed to be a case of history repeating itself for her fleet mate, the *European Gateway*, had capsized in similar circumstances in 1982, following a collision. In saying this, it is, perhaps, hinted that the forces of chance or destiny have had some influence on the turn of events-for it might be assumed that all necessary action to prevent a repeat occurrence had been taken. This was most definitely not the case, however, as the subsequent inquiry revealed. Just as is so often the case, history's apparently disconcerting habit of repeating itself where the *Herald of Free Enterprise* was concerned had more to do with the fact that there had been a persistent failure to learn the lessons from earlier disaster experiences, including that of the *European Gateway*. Nor, it seems, had there been a willingness to apply or impose changes in the light of such experiences to prevent further incidents.

    Both of these ships were roll-on-roll-off type vessels with vast, unpartitioned car decks. In the event of flooding there was little to minimise or prevent general ingress of water, creating the danger of a free surface of tons of highly mobile water which rendered the ship

dangerously unstable.

The *Herald of Free Enterprise* had apparently put to sea with her bow doors still open, a widely followed practice of many cross-Channel operators up to that time, in order to maintain her competitively tight schedules. In fairness, "but for the grace of God", it could have been one of many other ships that ended up in this plight. Water that entered the car deck through the open doors rapidly provided the first ingredient for creating dangerous instability. The necessary manoeuvres to follow the meandering deep water channel out of Zeebrugge provided the second, and the fatal blow was struck.

Ironically, had the ship been able to keep to a straight course, there was a possibility, though extremely remote, that the vessel might have survived as the water gradually escaped through her scuppers. On the other hand, as already stated, the course changes so early on realistically meant the difference between the heavy death toll that there was and the even bigger one if the ship had gone down in deep water.

The arrival of the rescue services meant that, for those who had survived, relief from their frightening ordeal was soon at hand. The quite terrible experiences that some passengers had suffered were soon to be revealed to the public at large as the news reverberated around the world. Imagine everything suddenly turning through 90 degrees, as you are plunged into total darkness, and all loose objects, including yourself and the people around you, tumbling over and over to end up a chaotic mêlée over which icy water was rapidly flooding.

Incredible stories of bravery and heroism emerged from the survivors. Some had clambered across disoriented passageway walls in pitch darkness only to encounter the gaping holes of athwartships gangways at the bottom of which was black icy water and certain death. Human bridges were organised in order to permit these hazards to be crossed. For others, it was a case of being trapped at levels which were already partly flooded with no way of knowing whether the water had risen to its maximum extent or whether they were facing a slow and agonising death by drowning.

Many families had been split up in those first terrifying seconds as, in time honoured fashion, passengers had been preparing for the voyage in their various ways. Youngsters had been exploring the ship, parents were checking out the duty free shops or changing the last of their foreign currency. Now they were separated, parents from children, husbands from wives, anxious for their well-being amid the moaning and sobbing that reached out of the cold blackness. And all around lay the many, unidentifiable bodies of the less fortunate.

If ever a disaster was characterised by the intensity of the human drama, it was that of the *Herald of Free Enterprise* and throughout the subsequent salvage the ramifications of the concern over this aspect of the incident were to have a profound and undiminishing influence. With the

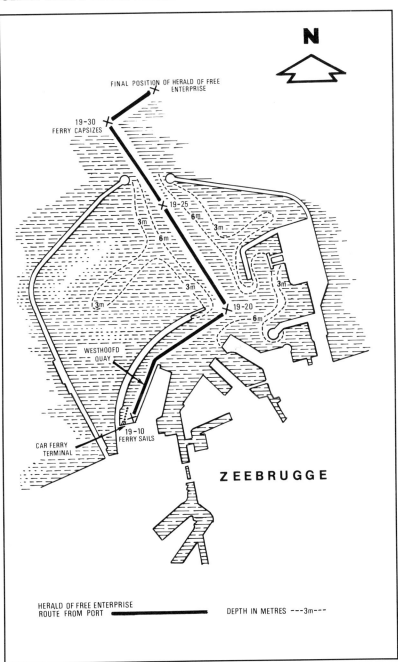

N

FINAL POSITION OF HERALD OF FREE ENTERPRISE

19-30
FERRY CAPSIZES

19-25

3m   6m

6m   3m

6m

3m

3m   3m

3m   19-20
6m

WESTHOOFD QUAY

19-10
FERRY SAILS

CAR FERRY TERMINAL

ZEEBRUGGE

HERALD OF FREE ENTERPRISE
ROUTE FROM PORT ━━━━━━━   DEPTH IN METRES ---3m---

41

(above): The Herald of Free Enterprise's *route out of Zeebrugge showing the position where she came to rest.*

cold light of day came the first opportunity to assess the situation - the progress of the rescue, the inevitable head counts and publication of the numbers of fatalities and survivors. But this latter proved to be quite impossible for, apart from the other failures of the ship's crew and owners that were progressively revealed, it became clear that only an inaccurate and incomplete passenger manifest had been made. Not only was it impossible to state categorically how many had not survived but the precise number of persons that had been aboard was not even certain. To name any one person that was still missing was, it seemed, totally out of the question.

For anyone in Great Britain who had friends or relatives travelling by ship from the Continent, whose precise plans were not known, an agonizing wait now followed until the salvors could raise the ship and remove the bodies for identification.

So it was that, when Smit Tak, who were awarded the salvage contract in conjunction with the Union de Remorquage et de Sauvetage and the Tijdelijke Vereniging van Bergingswerken, commenced work on lifting the vessel, the overriding priority was the retrieval of the bodies of victims; the progress of the operation was dominated by this factor. Issues of safety had to be re-evaluated in the light of this concern in order to achieve a rapid result. Work only stopped when the salvage team themselves were at risk, rather than when the ship itself might suffer and be less worthy of repair for further service.

Due to the human interest of the accident, all work had to be conducted under the ever watchful eye of the world's press.

Smit Tak was on the scene in less that 24 hours from the time that the *Herald of Free Enterprise* had turned over, rendering assistance from units of the company's vast fleet of vessels, based just up the coast in the Netherlands. Also, acutely aware of the unfolding issue over the failure to report accurately the casualties, Smit Tak personnel had been making a preliminary survey so as to be ready to offer a prompt solution when it was called for. When the salvage contract was awarded to them, on 8 March, they were able to commence work immediately.

In the final few seconds, prior to coming to a dead stop, the Herald had wandered, out of control, out of the main channel. She was now lying in approximately 11 metres (36 feet) of water on a sloping sand bank, listing about 3 degrees beyond the horizontal. Fortunately, she had not initially become buried in the sand and silt of the sea bed although her underside, which was hard on the bottom, was largely inaccessible.

This presented the salvors with a rather more complex task than might otherwise have been the case. The preferred technique for righting and lifting a ship in this situation would have been to seal it and pump it dry, gradually turning it in a controlled manner as it returned to the surface. However, to access and seal all underside openings, working through the ship from the inside, would have taken an unacceptable

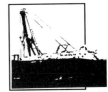

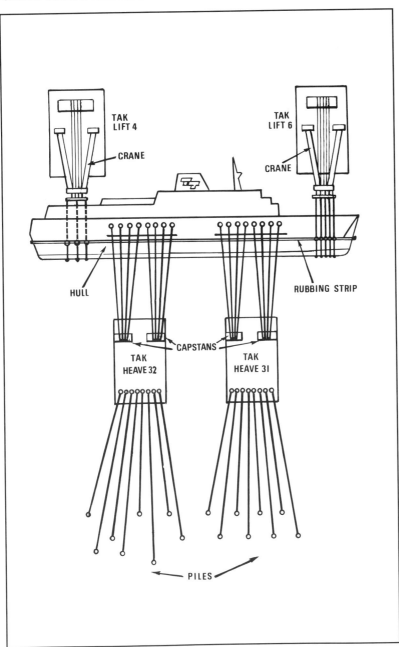

43

(above): Plan view of the salvage site showing the positions of the Herald of Free Enterprise, *the two sheerlegs, the two pullbarges and the various connections between the craft.*

amount of time in the circumstances. The only alternative was to attempt to lift the ship bodily using pull-barge winches and floating crane sheerlegs, applying sufficient power both to raise and rotate the vessel simultaneously. This would be no mean feat, depending for success on the most precise calculations and still necessitating considerable preparatory work on site.

As it turned out, a combined righting and raising operation was not possible and the two manoeuvres had to be carried out separately. The salvage operation that ensued had a number of distinct phases:

1. Detailed planning of the salvage to determine and pro gramme the logistics of equipment supply for each successive phase.

2. Assembling, testing and commissioning of equipment.

3. Preparing the *Herald of Free Enterprise.*

4. Stationing and preparing the support and salvage vessels.

5. Connecting everything together in readiness for,

6. Righting and stabilising the *Herald of Free Enterprise.*

7. Fitting pumps and sealing.

8. Pumping-out and floating the *Herald of Free Enterprise.*

44

In reality, many phases overlapped as the operation progressed, its momentum governed by the fight against time. Equally, certain phases and in particular those concerned with the preparation of the ferry and other vessels were extremely complicated, breaking down into additional sub-stages.

Wire lines would have to be strategically attached to the ship, requiring padeye strong points and guide rails to be welded along her starboard side around the longitudinal centre of gravity. A number of piles had to be sunk and wires attached to them to give the pull-barges something to pull against. Reaction anchors had to be positioned on the sea-bed and connected to the ferry to control its movement during the critical righting phase.

In essence, the technique that Smit Tak finally elected to employ consisted of two elements. First, returning the *Herald of Free Enterprise* to an upright position while she still remained settled on the bottom.

CHAPTER 3

Using two sets of sheerlegs and two pull-barges the ferry would be gradually rotated into the vertical. Then, while temporarily suspended in this upright situation, divers would patch the vessel for pumping out and refloating. It was hoped that an examination of the interior might prove to be possible prior to the final lifting stage.

As all of the lifting, stability and stress calculations were being verified by technical experts at Smit Tak's headquarters in Rotterdam, emergency project teams were assembled, one to remain resident in the headquarters building, the other to be on site at Zeebrugge. Simultaneously, the fleet of salvage vessels mobilised for the task began to arrive at the scene. Many different types of craft were required - the floating sheerleg cranes *Taklift 4* (2,400 tonnes lift), *Taklift 6* (1,600 tonnes lift) and, for backup, the *Norma* (425 tonnes lift); the pull-barges *Takheave 31* and *Takheave 32*, each with a pull force capability of 3,000 tonnes; the diving support vessels *Deurloo* and *Orca*, which served respectively as the work platforms for the underwater and welding activities. Apart from these major vessels, there were many other smaller craft, including the tugs *Fighter*, *Union III* and *Walvis*.

Along with the salvage vessels came much of the equipment necessary for the operation - generators, compressors, pumps and cutting and welding gear.

The computer calculations of the stress forces that would be imposed on the *Herald of Free Enterprise* during the righting phase raised questions about the vulnerability of the ferry's superstructure. Not only had the weight of the ferry to be moved but also the weight of the significant amount of water now contained within her hull. Utilising the pull-barges in conjunction with the sheerlegs, the latter in effect taking the weight of the ship, would distribute the load in the most satisfactory manner. Numerous strong points had to be welded to the ferry's quite fragile hull, though, to strengthen it sufficiently before the righting process could proceed. This work now commenced in earnest.

Work on the *Herald* commenced on 10 March but had to be stopped almost immediately when it was discovered that poisonous fumes were escaping from the cargo compartments. By 12 March the seawater and atmosphere surrounding the wreck had been tested and the all clear given, permitting work to recommence. The condition of the water and the air were regularly monitored throughout the remainder of the operation.

Welding of the first strong points now began. Initially, it was determined that a total of 42 would have to be fixed in place, 32 for the pull-barge and sheerleg connections and 10 for securing reaction anchors to prevent movement of the wreck. Progress was good with 26 welded by the end of 14 March and all work completed just two days later. An additional 8 strong points, later found to be necessary, were welded into place by 26 March. At the same time 18 guide rail supports were being

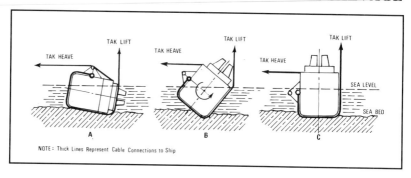

NOTE: Thick Lines Represent Cable Connections to Ship

46

(top): The technique employed to right the Herald of Free Enterprise, *indicating the directions of the respective pull efforts applied by the sheerlegs and the pullbarges.*

The righting operation in progress: (above left): the ferry partly rotated. (left): Coming over ...

(bottom left): The righted ferry showing the wire slings attached to one of the craft Taklift. All Leo van Ginderen.

positioned and welded along the ferry's sides. On to these cantilevered guide rails would be attached, in two 25 metre (82 feet) sections, each of which was to have its U-sectioned upper side filled with cement to give it extra strength.

Meanwhile, the plan for the pull-barge mooring system had been finalised. This involved driving 16 steel piles deep into the sea-bed some distance from the wreck's starboard side. Later, the pull-barges would be positioned between the two and secured to the piles. Clearance for pile driving was granted by the Zeebrugge Port Authority on 14 March. Before the day was out, driving had started and the first pile was in place.

Between 17 and 21 March, severe weather forced the abandonment of almost all work. Strong winds with heavy rain and pounding waves made working on the ferry's exposed side unacceptably hazardous. Pile driving was made more difficult as the vessels involved could not maintain position over each pile as it was being driven down. Besides, there was a danger of disturbing those that had already been positioned.

The salvage operation was repeatedly interrupted by bad weather during the preparation phase and, later too, during the righting and lifting phases. The problem was, perhaps, more critical during the initial stages of the operation for it caused the wreck to move. This, in turn, necessitated constant corrective action by Smit Tak in order to ensure that everything was correctly placed before the salvage proper commenced.

47

By 21 March, when the first spell of bad weather had cleared, the ferry's foreship had moved 3 metres (9.75 feet) to the west, her midships 3 metres (9.75 feet) to the east and the aft by 5.7 metres (18.75 feet) to the east. The hull had also now penetrated the sea-bed up to as much as a metre (3.25 feet) deep in places. Following a second stormy period between 27 and 31 March she moved even further. The bow moved another 5.8 metres (19 feet) to the west, the midships 3.8 metres (12.5 feet) further to the east and aft by another 8.4 metres (27.5 feet) to the east. Simultaneously, her list increased as she sank 2.5 metres (8.25 feet) deeper into the sea-bed. Huge waves driven by gale force winds were responsible for this, forces beyond the control of the salvage team.

During the period of adverse weather, divers had fitted netting over the bow and stern doors to prevent loose obstacles from falling out. They had already discovered trucks and trailers on the sea-bed which had been removed but clearly if any others became dislodged this would present a serious hazard to divers and could impede the progress of the operation. The netting over the stern door was later strengthened.

With the resumption of all work on 22 March, the pile driving and guide rail construction efforts were stepped up. By the end of 23 March all the piles were in place although two of them had to be driven down an extra metre (3.25 feet) on 25 March. The forward section of the cantilevered guide rail, which was lifted aboard in two 12.5 metre (41 feet) sections, was also finished the same day.

Though the wind had abated, work had to be suspended again, for other reasons, on 24 March. Torrential rain made the side of the hull dangerously slippery for the welders to work on so the salvage team was compelled temporarily to abandon this work.

All in all, 26 March was a very productive day for on that day the reaction anchors, which had been brought from Rotterdam on 17 March aboard *Union III* and positioned on 22 March, were fully connected to the *Herald of Free Enterprise* while all remaining welding work was also completed.

Having finished all preparation work on the site and aboard the stricken ferry, Smit Tak's next task was to connect everything up with ropes and cables, from the sheerlegs to the bow and stern strongpoints, from the pull-barges over the cantilevers to the midships strongpoints and from the pull-barges to the anchor piles. This work occupied the salvage team from 1 to 6 April.

Two problems were encountered in the course of this. First, difficulty was experienced in passing messenger wires under the aft end of the *Herald of Free Enterprise*. To these would be attached the cables that would link the *Taklift 4* to the aft strongpoints. A special pump had to be brought on site to clear a passage beneath the vessel through which the messenger wires could be passed. Secondly, the *Taklift 4* could not be brought sufficiently close to the wreck to apply lift in the direction required. This was due to debris and projections from the ferry that impeded positional movement. During 3 April divers cleared all of this including the removal of the *Herald's* aft mast.

To prevent more water entering the ship, after she had been turned, the scuppers along the starboard side of E deck were cemented over.

The critical righting operation commenced at 08.20 on 7 April. It went entirely according to plan and was completed by 18.35 the same day, at which time the salvors announced that the *Herald of Free Enterprise* was once more in a vertical position with her keel on the sea-bed. Throughout the righting process there had been a halt at every 10 degrees of rotation to permit stability checks to be made.

The next stage of the salvage involved the restoration of the ferry's buoyancy, utilising the sheerlegs to hoist her while she was being pumped out. This necessitated the attachment of lifting slings which could only be accomplished by a certain amount of detachment of the existing connections along with a re-arrangement of the salvage vessels.

Although there was continuing concern about the ferry's stability, as she was now precariously positioned at the top of an incline on the sea-bed, it was agreed that investigation teams should now be permitted to enter the ship to commence the recovery of bodies. Already a month had passed since the accident, with the salvage operation somewhat behind the projected timetable due to long spells of inclement weather. The wait for news was becoming unbearable for the victims' families. Between 8 and

CHAPTER 3

12 April, 115 bodies were located and brought ashore at the Zeebrugge naval base for identification. At this point the weather once more turned bad forcing the termination of the search.

While the work of recovering bodies was proceeding, the salvage team busied itself with the preparation for raising the *Herald of Free Enterprise*. To minimise the strain on the sheerlegs, efforts were made to reduce the volume of water trapped inside the vessel. On 11 April holes were cut in the ship's port side on C deck to release some of the water and to provide access for submersible pumps to shift water from even lower levels.

Smit's salvage log for 13 April reads simply "No activities. Weather extremely bad", something of an understatement when one considers that the anchorage was battered continually for almost 24 hours by storm force winds. An appraisal of the situation on the following day revealed that the ferry's position had moved 16 metres (52.5 feet) to the east and 10 metres (32.75 feet) in the direction of the harbour entrance. She was now listing 15.4 degrees to port and had sunk almost 3 metres (9.75 feet) into the sea-bed. Structural damage had occurred too with plating smashed in several places and a number of windows and watertight doors destroyed. Much of Smit's equipment had also suffered with welding sets and other tackle lost in the sea. Much of the vital preparatory work for lifting the ship had been nullified.

Pending the commencement of the lifting phase, the Smit salvage team was preoccupied with the struggle to prevent the *Herald of Free Enterprise* from slipping into the trough in the sea-bed alongside which she was now perilously balanced. If the ship was to slip into this deeper water, the whole salvage operation would be set back and take months longer to complete with all the attendant increase of anguish that this would cause. With much of her port side still unsealed the ferry would be in danger of flooding to a considerably higher level but worse still, in her unstable state, she could even roll back over on to her side. The team were also concerned with inhibiting the wreck's gradual settlement into the sea bottom.

Hampered by extremely strong currents and occasional breaks in the weather, the re-arrangement of the salvage craft was finally completed and wire slings secured aboard the *Herald*. The *Takheave 32* was positioned astern of her, to pull her in that direction while the sheerlegs were applying lift. At one point, when the wind reached Beaufort force 8, all the wires had to be disconnected again to prevent chaffing and weakening.

On 23 April, with all pumps positioned on board and checked, the lifting operation began. As the sheerlegs and the barge strained in unison, the *Herald of Free Enterprise* was first moved 29 metres (95 feet) to the west, away from the trough, while her list immediately reduced to only 3 degrees. Working at full power, the pumps were removing, in

combination, some 3 million kilograms (3,500 tons) of water per hour so that, by the following morning, buoyancy was restored to the ferry's aft end.

Smit Tak were not happy with the rate of water removal, however, and later the same day the salvage operation was again, temporarily, stopped while the company sought means of improving the pumping capacity. Holes were burned in the forward port side plating of E deck to allow access to G deck where an additional 8-inch pump was placed. Patching work was simultaneously carried out elsewhere on E deck while the opportunity was also taken to reposition further the wire slings attached to *Taklift 4* and *Taklift 6*. On resumption, the pumping capacity had been increased to 5 million kilograms (5,000 tons) per hour.

The *Herald of Free Enterprise* was fully refloated on 27 April, though still supported by the slings attached to the sheerlegs. Pumping was continuing and a correx preservation team went aboard to commence efforts to save the ship's main engines, generators and steering gear. While the primary objective of the salvage had thus far been the recovery of the victims of the accident, Smit Tak were now proceeding with efforts to save the ship itself in accordance with routine practice.

The whole ensemble of sheerlegs craft and the supported ferry were towed into Zeebrugge where they were anchored in the outer harbour. Here, the efforts to secure the stricken ferry and to discharge and clean it continued prior to its transfer to the Scheldepoort Flushing for dry docking. The task of locating the remaining bodies also now resumed and in some parts of the vessel, notably F deck, on the port side aft, holes had to be cut in the hull so that mud and debris could be removed to facilitate the search.

On 6 May the *Taklift 4* was relieved by the *Taklift 1*. The following day the *Taklift 6* disconnected altogether and entered the inner harbour at Zeebrugge. By 12 May the *Herald* had been completely cleared and cleaned. The holes, cut in her sides had been sealed and the blocked scuppers on E deck had been re-opened. Her forward and aft rudders were secured in the amidships position.

The next day the *Herald of Free Enterprise* was determined as floating without assistance. Hence, the *Taklift 1* was also disconnected and, following the final survey of the ship by the Salvage Association and the issuing of a towage certificate, she was formally handed over to her owners. Later that same day the *Herald* left Zeebrugge under tow, bound for Flushing Roads. With the clearance of the anchorage site and the removal of the piles from near the fairway into Zeebrugge, the Smit Tak operation was wound up.

Yet again, under the most demanding circumstances, salvage had been promptly and efficiently effected. Amid the emotion and debate Smit Tak had quietly, professionally and sympathetically gone about their business, expeditiously preparing the ship for the heart-rending

search of its mud choked, darkened interiors. Afterwards the company had delivered the ship, according to contract, for whatever fate awaited it.

If the exercise is reviewed from a salvage standpoint, then little more can be added to what has already been written. From the safety at sea angle, though, much remains to be said and done. The Government inquiry focused on the deficiencies of the *Herald of Free Enterprise's* officers and crew as well as on the low standard of general management and direction displayed by Townsend Thoresen.

Some legislation was introduced that compelled owners to take certain classes of ferry, whose stability was suspect, out of service within a stipulated period. The maintenance of accurate passenger manifests was also mandated. But the much more serious, underlying design weakness of the ro-ro ferry type, developed from commercially advantageous exploitation of existing tonnage and loadline legislation, remains to be positively addressed.

It is essential that the rules that relate to the sub-division and damaged-state stability of conventional ships should not be applied to ro-ro vessels. Until such time as this change to maritime law and the Solas Convention is introduced, the situation remains one of another potentially horrific accident waiting to happen and history, once more, will repeat itself.

For its part, P & O, the owners of Townsend Thoresen, had their entire fleet of cross-Channel ferries renamed, doing away with the emotive words "FREE ENTERPRISE" that they had all carried and which the press had made a great deal of, suggesting that profits had been put before passenger safety.

The *Herald of Free Enterprise* was herself renamed but not in readiness for a resumption of service. Despite Smit Tak's efforts she was found to be beyond economic recovery. Declared a constructive total loss, she was sold for breaking up in the Far East. Renamed *Flushing Range* she left under tow of the tug *Markursturm* in late 1987 in consort with the *Gaelic Ferry,* another coastal passenger ship bound for the scrap yard. The tow was not without its drama either, for first in the Bay of Biscay and later, off Port Elizabeth, South Africa, the two ferries broke their tow in bad weather and were left drifting out of control. After the second incident the *Markursturm* was relieved of her duties and the tow was completed by the tug *Sirocco.*

51

(left): The righted ferry showing the wire slings attached to one of the craft Taklift Leo van Ginderen.

Artefacts and Archives

All around the British coast and in other sea areas worldwide where shipping traffic has traditionally concentrated, there are numerous, and uncountable, ancient and historic ship wrecks. These wrecks are time capsules of the maritime past; clues to the pattern of seaborne trade in centuries long obscured by the mists of time. They are also potential treasure chests.

On the one hand they can yield a wealth of valuable artefacts, rare objects which are highly collectable and which command a high price due to their rarity.

On the other hand these same wrecks can contribute immensely to our knowledge of historic cultures and civilisations through the systematic excavation of underwater sites as a whole, treating every element as important whether or not it has any financial value.

52

Both these approaches to recovery from the sea constitute salvage but the latter is a particularly specialised form of salvage involving numerous techniques peculiar to this work.

Whereas the treasure hunter generally has little difficulty in generating the funds to finance his searches, the disposal of artefacts providing a highly lucrative source of income, the marine archaeologist encounters immense problems in obtaining financial support for his work. The archaeologist's objective is to protect wreck sites as a cultural resource for the community, although this is frequently misunderstood or not necessarily appreciated, but because he is not self-sustaining and depends on sponsorships and hand-outs he is seen too often as indulging self-interest. He is also seen as an irritant by the treasure hunter and amateur sports diver, beset with high and mighty principles, denying them the right to make a bit of money on the side in pursuit of their hobby. This conflict of interests is sometimes deep and bitter, each point of view vigorously defended by its respective protagonists.

There is perhaps no better example of this contrast of attitudes than the rivalry between George Bass, the eminent American professor of nautical archaeology, and Melvin Fisher of Treasure Salvors Incorporated, Key West, Florida, whose "finders, keepers" philosophy has resulted in no less than 111 appearances in the state courts.

This chapter looks at the issue from the archaeologist's standpoint, partly because of the special survey and preservation techniques employed but also because, as a maritime nation, the investigation and

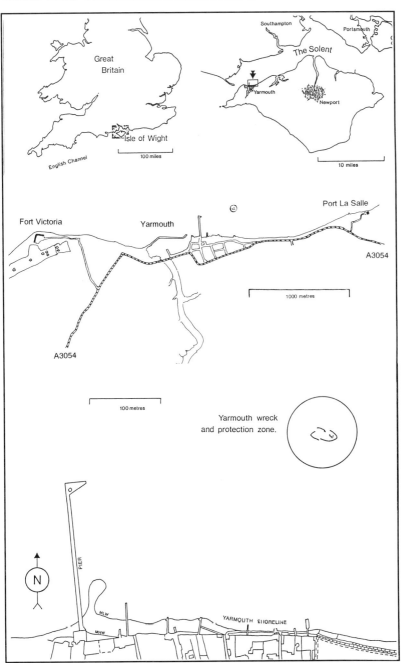

53

(above): Map of Yarmouth, Isle of Wight, showing the site of the medieval wreck in relation to the project bases at Port La Salle and Fort Victoria.

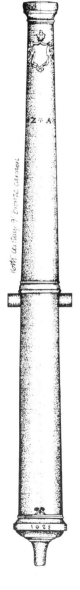

North elevation of bronze cannon.

preservation of our underwater history as a bequest to future generations is vitally important.

In reality, the archaeological teams working on the sea-bed are sincere, highly-motivated groups who are frustrated at the indiscriminate plundering of our maritime heritage for personal gain which, in spite of the existence of quite punitive legal statutes, is difficult to prevent. This sense of frustration is compounded by the lack of a co-ordinated policy on wreck protection and excavation between all the organisations, official, professional and voluntary, expressly concerned with maritime conservation. A further obstacle is the reticence of private concerns to support valuable but unglamorous activities which do not attract appropriate publicity.

One such archaeological salvage operation that has pioneered totally unique concepts in underwater excavation and preservation is the Maritime Heritage Project based at Yarmouth, Isle of Wight. It has experienced acute funding problems in the furtherance of its efforts, in spite of quite radical ideas on achieving financial self-sufficiency.

The story began in 1984 when, purely by chance, an ancient wreck was discovered just to the east of Yarmouth pier in 6 metres (19.5 feet) of water. It was then little more than a series of lines of timber frames protruding a few centimetres from the sea-bed. Initial recoveries of artefacts, mainly pewter plates strewn amongst the wreck timbers, permitted a tentative dating of the wreck to the 17th century. From these somewhat meagre preliminary revelations, however, a significant, three-pronged archaeological salvage project developed.

First, and perhaps foremost, was the effort to obtain protected status for the wreck followed by the full-scale recovery of artefacts from the wreck site, possibly to culminate in the lifting and reconstruction of the wreck itself, if it was sufficiently intact. Simultaneously, investigations into the vessel's identity were initiated, a revealing process which always promised surprises. Finally, and to some extent in parallel with these main activities due to the need to fund the work, was the formation of the Project itself as an organised body with somewhat broader objectives, not least of which was a fundamental re-think on the entire approach to underwater conservation in the United Kingdom. These strategic objectives emerged, were defined and even redefined as events unfolded.

Almost simultaneous with the discovery of the wreck was the recovery from the same vicinity of an elegant bronze cannon with the remnants of its wooden carriage. The crest and initials on its muzzle showed that the gun had been cast in Italy in the 16th century by a Venetian named Zuanne Alberghetti. By implication, if the cannon came from the wreck, then the vessel in question was a lot older than had been originally thought. The subsequent recovery of two spoons made from latten, a pewter alloy, and judged to date from circa 1500, raised the possibility

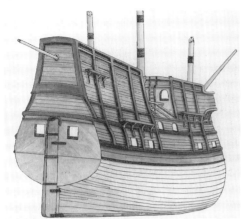

(left): Artist's impression of the carrack Santa Lucia. She was estimated to measure 70 feet from her keel to the main mast truck, 35 to 40 feet to the stern castle. If the water depth at the time of the loss was roughly the same as today, then much of the ship would have been visible above the surface of the sea. Maritime Heritage Project

55

(left): Pottery artefacts from the Yarmouth Roads wreck. Maritime Heritage Project.

(left): Pewter plates and latten spoon from the wreck. Maritime Heritage Project.

that the wreck, if contemporary with these objects, was even older still, perhaps older than the *Mary Rose*. If so, it was a discovery of major historical importance.

The Isle of Wight Archaeological Committee, a grant funded group having charitable status, under the leadership of Dr. David Tomalin, set up an initial, one year project to research the wreck. This was principally to conduct a pre-disturbance survey, to determine the full extent of the wreck and whether it warranted the slow and costly process of full excavation. This was to be followed by the excavation of a preliminary trench across the wreck at what was thought to be its stern end.

An application was made to the Runciman Committee of the Department of Transport to have the Yarmouth Roads wreck protected under the terms of the Protection of Wrecks Act, 1973. This was duly granted, permitting work to commence on the wreck beginning with marking the site with a round yellow buoy bearing the words "Protected wreck".

The Maritime Heritage Project was formally constituted in 1986 as agents of the Isle of Wight Archaeological Committee and granted a licence to survey and excavate the wreck. In passing it should be mentioned that the Department of Transport's Archaeological Diving Unit regularly checks such historical salvage sites to ensure that licensing arrangements and operations are being carried out in accordance with the regulations of the Act of Parliament.

Initially, funding for the Maritime Heritage Project was derived through the Manpower Services Commission which provided for a staff of seven. This team was supplemented by volunteers, both divers and archaeological specialists. The Project was also provided with free accommodation in the old boat houses at Port La Salle, to the north-east of Yarmouth.

The wreck, which measured approximately 35 metres (115 feet) long overall, was lying barely 200 metres (655 feet) from the shore. Despite this, and the fact that it was submerged in only fairly shallow waters, other natural conditions peculiar to this coastal stretch made work on the wreck difficult and progress was consequently tediously slow. The Solent, at this point, experiences very strong currents and tidal movements that limit diving operations to neap tidal periods and then to only the hour or two of slack water at each high and low tide. Visibility is poor, worsened by the sediment of fine grey silt which surrounds the wreck site and which is readily disturbed by the slightest movement.

To help overcome these problems, some special techniques, based on the experience of earlier archaeological teams, were devised. For example, using materials supplied by local manufacturing concerns, a fluorescent grid of glowlines was laid across the wreck to guide divers.

The primary task in the pre-disturbance survey was the construction of a site plan, obtained by carefully measuring each timber and its position in relation to the whole site using a number of readily located datum points. In order to draw under water, the divers used pencils on permatrace sheets attached to metal or perspex clipboards. Accuracy of scale was achieved by using metre square aluminium drawing frames, strung at 10cm intervals, which were laid over the objects to be drawn.

Once complete, the site plan proved an invaluable tool for planning work and aiding diver orientation, essential if the maximum productive efficiency was to be derived from each diving sortie. The plan revealed that the wreck was lying in an east/west direction with her stern towards the Needles Channel, suggesting that the vessel had been inward bound at the time of the accident which caused her to sink. If this was so, then the absence of large quantities of artefacts also suggested that the bulk of her cargo had been salvaged at an earlier date.

As part of the pre-disturbance inspection a remote sensing survey was carried out to determine the depth of sediments over the site. This also provided vital clues as to the extent of the vessel's surviving structure. Remote sensing surveys are undertaken using a sub-bottom profiler which fires sound waves into the sea-bed. The waves penetrate the superficial sediments but reflect back off 'harder' anomalies or bedrock. The reflected waves are converted into a visual display which is used to interpret the composition of the sea- bed. In the case of the Yarmouth Roads wreck this confirmed that there was at least 2 metres (6.5 feet) of structure beneath the sea-bed.

57

By the close of the Project's first season considerable progress had been made in gathering the necessary information to decide whether future effort in excavating the wreck was merited. In all, divers had spent 392 hours working on the site. The site plan was complete, the remote sensing survey had provided valuable additional information and all the evidence suggested that further excavation was worthwhile for the wreck structure appeared to be coherent.

Thus, a programme for the second season was prepared with the emphasis on a closer examination of the wreck's integrity with salvage of the entire structure in mind; also, there would be an intensification of the search for clues as to the vessel's identity.

Extension of the Manpower Services Commission funding permitted an increase of Project staffing to twenty three, of whom nineteen were part-time. In spite of the welcome cushion of this government-sponsored assistance, the Project management was well aware that this could not be regarded as an unlimited resource and that, ultimately, the Project would have to derive its main income from other sources. Through its detailed examination of the Yarmouth Roads wreck site, the Project team had produced a unique and comprehensive profile of this area of the local sea-bed. It was known, too, from modern and ancient records, that the Solent and the general region of Isle of Wight coastal waters was probably unrivalled for its underwater archaeological

potential, there being over 800 wrecks recorded in these waters since 1298 and, probably, an equal number of other, unrecorded losses. Hence, for the first time, a permanent, self-funding Maritime Heritage Centre was mooted, dedicated to exploring and preserving the island's submerged historical sites as a whole. It would be promoted as the focal centre for all national maritime archaeological research and salvage, providing training in diving, excavation and preservation techniques. Further, to raise essential revenue, it would establish a major tourist attraction with museum displays and offering interactive amateur involvement in excavation projects. The seeds had been sown for a radical concept in the national conservation of our maritime history.

While the greater part of the second diving season was devoted to undertaking further exploratory excavations, time was also allocated to dealing with the backlog of artefact recording which had already built up and producing a computerised excavation archive. The archaeological record for the Yarmouth Roads wreck consists of written and visual archives which are sub-divided into four categories:

TIMBERS

SKELETONS

ARTEFACTS

CONTEXT *

Pre-printed standard report forms for each of these headings are completed by the divers after each sortie and the data is deposited into a computer in accordance with procedures formulated by the Central Excavating Unit, part of English Heritage's data management system.

This effort to maintain a permanent, detailed record of all features of the wreck site is time-consuming and, hence, a great drain on Project resources. Nevertheless, in the context of an archaeological salvage, it is essential that this is performed in a methodical, precise fashion for excavations, even those by trained archaeologists, are regarded as little more than the systematic destruction of the physical remains of the past. Those undertaking excavations are therefore duty bound to transform the archaeological record into a permanent, written and visual archive. It is in this respect that archaeological salvage is particularly distinguished from treasure hunting in which everything but the materially valuable is discarded and little effort is made to record the finds or their location.

The overall strategy of the second season's programme of work was to cut a number of additional trenches across the stern of the vessel, each

*(supporting, material evidence that relates the other finds to their environment.)

intended to provide specific information.

The second trench was to investigate the sea-bed stratigraphy and, hopefully, provide an answer as to whether or not the structure had been preserved at a greater depth than that immediately below the surface.

The third concentrated on the newer sediments around the ship's stern to see whether remnants of her cargo or crews' possessions could be found that might reveal more conclusively the vessel's date or nationality and, thereby, her identity.

Finally, a fourth trench was intended to establish with greater certainty the wreck's integrity by checking whether those portions exposed above the sediments were connected beneath the sea-bed.

Completing this work occupied the bulk of the summer of 1988. Simultaneously, effort was intensified in the search into the vessel's origins for it was felt that future financial support might be dependent on definite identification, especially if she should have glamorous connections. Of course, authentication of the ship was an equally important aspect of the scientific study.

The second season's excavations produced a number of intriguing artefacts but little of intrinsic value. However, certain of these items offered real possibilities as avenues of enquiry in the quest to name the ship.

Pottery finds from the site were found to be made of a material known as majolica which was widely used in northern Italy during the latter half of the 16th century. The presence of several trefoil spouted

59

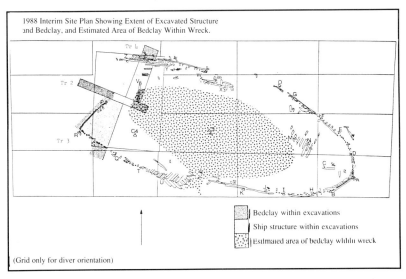

(above): Site plan of the Yarmouth Roads wreck showing renches 2, 3 and 4 that were cut by the Maritime Heritage Project divers. Maritime Heritage Project

jugs, with attractive lead and tin glazes which originally had been finished in green and blue on white, suggested that the pottery may have been cargo or the possessions of passengers for it was far too delicate for common ship use. (The pottery found aboard wrecked galleons of the Great Armada was a crude brown-glazed earthenware.)

More pewter plates and spoons were uncovered, some bearing a touchmark but this proved to be impossible to match with that of any known manufacturer or owner.

A bronze grinding mortar that was located proved a useful find. It was almost identical to another recovered from the Spanish ship *Trinidad Valencera*, one of the ill-fated Armada ships lost on the Irish coast. This provided the best confirmation yet that the Yarmouth Roads wreck originated from around the middle to late 16th century. There was, perhaps, even greater significance to this association for the *Trinidad Valencera* had been built as a large Venetian merchant ship only to be later pressed into the service of the King of Spain.

A number of turned wooden objects found on the wreck intrigued the Project team until they were identified as parts of a lantern very similar to one depicted in Pieter Breughel's painting "The Gloomy Day", dating from 1565. (Pieter Breughel the Elder was a Flemish painter who lived from 1520 to 1569).

60

Armed with this information, Alison Gale, Development Officer for the Maritime Heritage Project, set off to search through whatever official records that still existed in a bid to pinpoint a ship that fitted the description - Mediterranean trading vessel, probably a large carrack, sunk off the entrance of Yarmouth harbour in the late 1500s (Note: Carracks were two or three-masted medieval merchant sailing ships of varying size with square main sails and a lateen, triangular, sail on the mizzenmast).

No systematic recording of ship losses took place until the 19th century when the Board of Trade commenced the collection of casualty statistics. Lloyd's records date from 1746, so they were inappropriate in this instance, being of too recent vintage. Locating the identity of this much earlier wreck depended on someone at the time having enforced the legal 'right of wreck' in a case heard before a local Vice Admiralty Court or, if a very serious matter, before the High Court of the Admiralty.

Anything found floating in the sea or lying on the sea-bed or washed up on a beach was 'wreck' and ownership could be claimed by the sovereign of the day or a local landowner who had been granted 'right or wreck'. Records of disputes over 'right of wreck' survive from as far back as the 13th century. They provide much valuable information about vessels which have sunk around our coast and which would otherwise remain totally anonymous. Unfortunately, these records are scattered among various collections of ancient documents - among the papers of landed families, with the correspondence of the sovereign's ministers at the Public Record Office in London, in local County Record Offices or in

the minutes of the High Court of the Admiralty.

As such a ship, lying only 200 metres (655 feet) from the shore in shallow waters, had apparently been comprehensively stripped of her cargo there was a good probability that she had been the subject of a legal settlement over 'right of wreck'. So Alison Gale opted to concentrate her search in the Admiralty Records, an intuitive decision that deserved and was rewarded with positive results. The following accounts relating to a salvage dispute settlement refer to a ship that appears to fit the description of the Yarmouth Roads wreck in all respects:

'Saturday 31 January in the said year (1567/8) Anthony De Gwarras, Spanish merchant, residing in the City of London, and gave recognisance to Edward Horsey, Esq Vice Admiral of the Isle of Wight in the sum of £300 (due on) 1 March 1567/8.

The condicion of this recognisance ys suche that the above bounden merchant de Gwarras or one Jhon De Castro merchante of Burges in Flanders havinge of late obtayned commyssion from the Quenes highnes Courte of her Admiraltie for the recoverye of certyn wolls (wool) lately perished before the Isle of Wight in a Spannishe Shipp called *ST LUCIA* do stand unto performe and fulfill suche ordre and decre as the bove doctor Lewes judge of the said courte shall awarde sett and give ffor and concerninge suche expenses and charges as are growinge due unto the said Edwarde Horsey and suche of tinhabitantes of the said Isle of Wight as have performed there labour and pains in and aboute the savinge and gatheringe together of the said wolls And thereuppon do content satysfie and paye unto the same Edward Horsey or his assignes suche charges as the said judge shall taxe awarde and give in that behalfe That then this present recognizance to be voide and of none effect Or els to stand in his whole vertue and strength'.

'Saturday 7 February in the Admiralty Court before Judge David Lewes in presence of one Roger Parker, Registrar, personally appeared Anthony de Gwarras, Spanish merchant, residing in the City of London, and gave recognisance unto Edward Fynes etc. Lord Clinton and Say, High Admiral of England (due on) 1 April 1568.

'The condicion of the recognizannce is suche that where of late one Spannishe shipp called *SANTA LUCIA* laden with wolls in followinge her iourney and voyadge towarde Fflannders by fortune pished and was lost in the seas twhart (thwarte - opposite a place on the coast) of yarmouthe in thIsle of wighte and at this present remaynthe soncken in the seas whereunto the said Lorde Admirall makethe clayme in the righte of his office as goods soncken and lienge under the water yf therefor at anye tyme hereafter yt shall appere and fall owte the wolls and other merchandizes in the same perished and soncken shipp or anye part thereof to belonge or appertayne by lawe or custome to the saide Admirall in the righte of the same hys office then if the bove said

61

recognitor do accomplishe fullfill shall give therein without coven fraude or further delay. That then etc Or ells etc.'

That the wreck lying in Yarmouth Roads was the *St Lucia* or *Santa Lucia* seemed pretty certain but confirmation of her identity depended on matching the archaeological finds to the features noted in these historical records, few though they were. Funds permitting, further investigations of historic Spanish documents could then follow to elicit details of the vessel's specific type, rigging and purpose.

Meanwhile, work at the salvage site was also progressing well though some of the revelations concerning the structural integrity of the wreck were disappointing. A great deal of preparation had been necessary before excavation work could begin. First, a 12 metre by 9 metre (39.5 feet by 29.5 feet) grid, constructed from bright yellow scaffolding poles supplied by the local Gas Board, was erected on the site to provide a stable platform from which divers could work. Assembled ashore and floated out to the wreck site before being sunk, it was clamped into position on legs driven deep into the sea-bed. Many hours were spent levelling the grid and measuring it into existing datum points to ensure the accurate location of all subsequent discoveries of artefacts.

62

To improve the divers' productivity during their brief periods of immersion, a number of underwater dredges were fabricated to supply extra muscle power in the removal of spoil from the site. Made from conventional domestic plumbing materials and powered by pumps loaned by the Island's Fire & Rescue Service, they worked like huge, open-ended vacuum cleaners. Later, these were replaced by compressor-driven air lifts donated by the Southern Gas Board.

As an experiment to assess the amount of information that could be recovered during one season's work using strategically placed trenches, the results of the 1988 programme exceeded the MHP team's expectations.

It was less encouraging, however, in its prognosis for any attempt to lift the wreck as a whole.

Trenches two and three revealed that the ship's structure lay in two separate portions within hollows in the bed-clay. Trench three also exposed a section of the stern and starboard side. Here the frames and planking, which were of carvel or edge-to-edge construction, are relatively intact but elsewhere they are dislodged. The worst affected areas are the knees and stringers which had originally provided strength to the vessel's transom stern. These timbers are collapsed and stained with rust indicating the points where the iron fastenings have corroded away.

The fourth trench exposed the ship's port side which proved to be the source of the majority of the pewter and pottery finds.

In spite of doubts having been cast over the viability of attempting recovery of the entire wreck, sufficient evidence had been gathered to

(left): Detail from Breughel's painting "The Gloomy Day" showing wooden lantern at bottom centre, with (bottom left) *the remains of the wooden lantern found on the Yarmouth Roads wreck and* (far left) *a modern replica carved by one of the MHP team to indicate how the lantern looked originally.* Maritime Heritage Project.

confirm the age, identity and historical value of the wreck. A more extensive salvage excavation was now merited in order to expand the limited knowledge of 16th century merchant ships and their trade. This period is a blind spot in our view of maritime history. Little is known of the construction of ships of this time, their sailing capabilities or the methods of stowage of cargoes. Whereas the Armada records provide considerable insight in to the characteristics of fighting ships and a unique invasion force from this era, there is very little in the way of archives concerning contemporary common merchant ships.

Fate has a way of dealing its blows when fortunes seem at their peak, however, and this was how it was for the Maritime Heritage Project. Suddenly, the Project found its support drastically diminished. Changes to the structuring of the Manpower Services Commission meant that the Community Programme source of assistance would be largely withdrawn from September 1988. Simultaneously, the Project was advised that it would have to quit the premises at Port La Salle as they were needed as part of a proposed leisure centre development to be carried out through the winter of 1988/1989.

The already uneven division of time and energy between salvage work and fund raising now had to be even more distorted in favour of ensuring financial survival. A 'New Development Strategy' was launched as a major campaign to raise funds with three key objectives.

First, the Project sought the extension of MSC funding to March 1989, irrespective of how much less it might be. Second, the support of sponsors from the commercial sector was to be vigorously pursued. Finally, the ambitious scheme for a permanent Maritime Heritage Centre was to be clarified and more actively promoted.

As it turned out, the success of the 'New Development Strategy' was only partial. Manpower Services Commission funding was extended to March 1989, at a reduced level, while a County Council grant for a further three years' work was obtained, but this was only sufficient to provide for two full-time posts and two part-timers. Despite much effort, no significant, long-term sponsorship arrangement has been concluded, presumably because the MHP operation does not offer the potential for publicity which seems to be a pre-requisite of these sorts of deal. Some financial backing was contributed by Sealink (UK) as a result of interest in a quantity of archaeological antiquities that were revealed during dredging work for the new ferry terminal at Fishbourne, Isle of Wight.

As warned, the Project was compelled to move its base in October 1988, being re-housed in the old battery at Fort Victoria, on the far side of Yarmouth. Fort Victoria is the property of the Isle of Wight County Council, controlled by the Planning and Cultural Services Departments. Consequently, it at least offers reasonable prospects for secure and permanent tenure but still it is far from ideal, with inadequate space for the proper storage of preserved artefacts, and quite unsuitable for the

continuation of diving operations. Thus the diving team and other specialist team members were obliged to disperse.

The plans for the permanent Maritime Heritage Centre, which are yet to be realised, deserve closer attention for they herald an innovative and radically different approach to the conduct and funding of historic maritime salvage.

In effect the Maritime Heritage Centre proposals comprise three elements - the role of the Centre, the strategy for its formation and the location of a suitable site followed by the physical construction of the building.

The role of the Centre would essentially follow the broader remit of the Maritime Heritage Project in that it would assume responsibility for all historical sites located in Isle of Wight waters. Working from ship loss records, such as the Historical Marine Archives of Lloyd's of London, the National Maritime Museum's shipwreck records and the Admiralty Hydrographic Department's records of structures located on the sea-bed, a detailed survey would be undertaken first. Site cards have already been issued, as in land archaeology, for all known ship losses, all discovered wrecks and all stray finds so far identified. This initiative, carried out in conjunction with the County Archaeologist, will result in the completion of what is already the very first county based Maritime Sites and Monuments Record (MSMR), an index of all sites of potential archaeological or historical interest lying in the coastal region for which the county is responsible. The majority of British counties maintain a Sites and Monuments Record (SMR) of land remains, ranging from castles and cottages to hillforts and barrows, but the complete record of maritime sites being generated by the Maritime Heritage Project is, at present, unique.

Besides the Centre's primary role of investigating and excavating historic wreck sites it would be a training school for archaeological salvage techniques. It would also be a tourist attraction with a museum of maritime archaeology: there would be displays of artefacts and the centre would offer visitors the opportunity to participate in excavation, preservation and research activities. The importance of this latter function is confirmed by the intention to establish it as the Centre's principal source of revenue. Further income would be derived from consultancy services that would be offered to other county authorities proposing to create an MSMR.

Due to the reduction of Manpower Services funding and uncertainty about other financial support, the Maritime Heritage Project has sought charitable trust status in order to advance the setting up of its permanent centre. This change of status, to the Isle of Wight Trust for Maritime Archaeology, was sponsored by and has been dependent for its progress on the Isle of Wight Archaeological Committee. Such applications must first be submitted to the Charity Commissioners, after which they have to

65

go to the Value Added Tax authorities for consideration. The progress of formation of the IoW trust has been a protracted and frustrating business, beset with numerous bureaucratic and legal impediments. Critical as it is, with the future of the entire Project dependent on the outcome, it has finally been accomplished but the appointment of trustees was still awaited at the time of writing.

The situation of the Maritime Heritage Project in mid-1989 was not encouraging. The team is run down and demoralised. The Project's work in connection with both the Yarmouth Roads wreck *Santa Lucia* and the countywide MSMR was incomplete. Nevertheless, the remaining team members were determined, in spite of all the difficulties, to realise all their objectives, which is a testament to their tenacity and dedication.

The reader may well be wondering why a chapter on the Maritime Heritage Project has been included in this book when it has, thus far, been only partially successful in securing prizes (and those secured which are neither valuable nor spectacular) and when it clearly does not rank with the other dramatic salvage operations described elsewhere in other chapters.

There are a number of very good reasons for this. Archaeological excavation from the sea-bed is a seriously neglected aspect of salvage concerned with the preservation of the evidence of our maritime past. In this case, which involves retrieval of factual data from ancient records as well as artefacts from the sea-bed, the team workers are pioneering new concepts and techniques. It is, too, one of the few operations for which it has been possible to compile a complete account of events, difficulties and all, peculiar to the smaller team engaged in routine, unglamorous and under-funded work, in contrast to the well-publicised, well-supported exercise typified by the *Mary Rose* salvage.

Concluding on a positive note, May 1989 saw the publication of proposals for a national policy for the protection of underwater archaeological sites, suggesting that, whatever else may happen, not all of the efforts of the Maritime Heritage Project have been in vain.

Entitled "Heritage at Sea", the proposal document represents the combined views of the National Maritime Museum, the National Archaeological Society, the Council for British Archaeology, the Institute of Field Archaeologists and the Society for Nautical Research. Collectively, they comprise the Joint Nautical Archaeology Policy Committee.

The document is lengthy and worthy of reading in its own right but among its recommendations the following are particularly worthy of note:

1.   That new legislation for the protection of underwater archaeological sites should be drafted, with provision for the establishment of a maritime heritage protection and co-

ordination agency whose primary brief would be the formulation of a coherent approach to the protection of underwater heritage.

2. That payments of fees and VAT based on the market value of items raised from the sea-bed, as required by the Merchant Shipping Act, 1894, should be waived in cases where the items are to be retained in publicly accessible collections. Also, that archaeological salvage should be more clearly distinguished from commercial salvage.

3. That the responsibilities of the Ministry of Defence, for historic naval wrecks, and the Foreign & Common wealth Office, for East India Company wrecks, should either be properly fulfilled or transferred to the new Maritime Heritage Agency.

4. That the Maritime Heritage Agency should be formed from the already existing Archaeological Diving Unit, a small team of archaeologists contracted to the Department of Transport for five years from April 1986. The Agency should be provided with sufficient staff and resources to permit it to fulfil satisfactorily all its functions.

67

5. That a National Inventory of Underwater Sites should be created as a central repository of all county-based Marine Sites and Monument Records similar to that compiled by the Maritime Heritage Project.

The "Heritage at Sea" document duly acknowledges the pioneering work of the Maritime Heritage Project. It also recognises the burdensome financial difficulties that salvage exercises of this kind experience. It consequently proposes criteria for selecting historic wreck sites of national importance which should receive first priority assistance for excavation work from available national budgets. These criteria are:

1. All wreck sites earlier in date than AD 1650.

2. Other wreck sites up to AD 1850 which retain a substantial and coherent element of ship structure or which are vessels of special historic importance.

3. Certain vessels of later date which demonstrate a significant advance in ship technology.

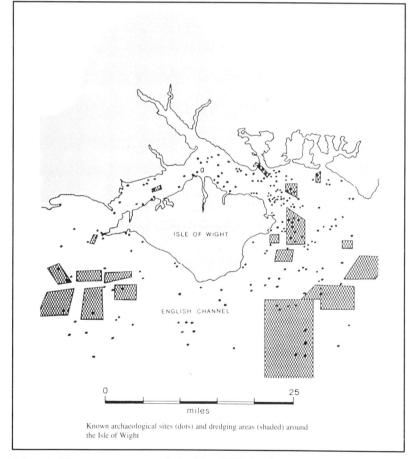

From this it is evident that the wreck of the *Santa Lucia* qualifies for inclusion under category 1 and that, under these arrangements, the Maritime Heritage Project would receive the assistance that it so desperately needs. While it is to be hoped that, in the event of the policy document being enacted, this will be the outcome, it does seem, if the interests of better financial prioritising are to be best served, that the criteria for selection should also give consideration to other factors. For example, the integrity of wrecks, regardless of their age, and, where sea-bed strata and working conditions are difficult, some estimated ratio of the likely reward to the effort that will have to be expended to achieve it. The Maritime Heritage Project will then be able to demonstrate its full potential, in the most ideal circumstances, as well as its ability, ultimately, to become self-sufficient.

68

ISLE OF WIGHT

ENGLISH CHANNEL

0   25

miles

Known archaeological sites (dots) and dredging areas (shaded) around the Isle of Wight

(above): The sea area around the Isle of Wight showing the concentration of archaeological wreck sites in these waters.

CHAPTER 5

From the Void of Space

The conquest of space really began in earnest when Major Yuri Gagarin was launched into near Earth orbit aboard his cramped spacecraft Vostok 1, just thirty years ago. The prospect of travel to the Moon seemed remote enough then yet was achieved in less than ten years and who, at that time, would have considered seriously that, by the mid-1980's salvage would be practised in space much as it had been at sea over centuries?

Space technology is certainly not cheap and the stakes involved in opening-up a commercial space industry for communications and weather satellites and other peaceful space applications have been huge. Indeed, such have been the immense amounts of money involved that early on space contractors sought insurance companies who were willing to underwrite their investments against the risk of loss; Lloyds Aviation Underwriters were among the pioneers in providing satellite insurance. By the late 1970's space had looked like rivalling the offshore oilfields as a profitable insurance business. However, the acute risks involved in these undertakings were exposed as early as 1979 when the market was hit by the loss of an £85 million satellite, at a time when rates were failing. Other expensive losses followed.

In these circumstances, the initiation of salvage of lost or damaged spacecraft, in circumstances where retrieval was both possible and appropriate, seemed inevitable. Since the underwriters were being asked to pay claims on what, otherwise, would be useless pieces of orbiting hardware, it was considered that if they could be recovered there was no reason why they could not claim them as salvage.

An opportunity to demonstrate what had become technologically attainable occurred in February 1984 when two satellites deployed by the space shuttle Challenger, on mission 41-B, failed to reach their destined geosynchronous orbits and were, consequently, rendered quite useless. As neither had been destroyed, recovery of the satellites for repair and future redeployment was an attractive possibility for consideration, both for insurance reasons and, from the US National Aeronautics & Space Agency's (NASA) point of view, to restore their credibility with other commercial payload customers following a sequence of embarrassing failures.

The communications satellites concerned were the *Palapa B-2*, commissioned by the Indonesian Government agency, Permutel, and the

Westar VI, owned by Western Union. Each satellite was insured for $100 million. Of the total amount, $180 million was covered by London underwriters. This represented a major loss to the insurance companies which would inevitably be passed on in increased premiums for future shuttle cargoes, posing yet a further potential deterrent to commercial satellite customers.

Like all such spacecraft launched by the space shuttle, these satellites had been placed initially in a 300 kilometre (186.5 mile) high, circular low-Earth orbit. The technique was then to place them in a so-called transfer orbit using a Payload Assist Module (PAM-D) which was attached to the base of each satellite. The PAM-D, built by McDonnell Douglas Astronautics, is a spherically-shaped, solid propellant motor complete with its own package of control electronics. Normal practice in deploying satellites is for the craft itself plus its boost stage to be set revolving by a spin table aboard the shuttle before being pushed away from the orbiting vehicle by springs. Forty-five minutes later the PAM-D motor is fired automatically carrying the craft into geosynchronous transfer orbit at which point, having completed its task, it separates from the spacecraft and is jettisoned. Later still, an apogee boost motor within the satellite itself converts the transfer orbit into the life-duration geosynchronous orbit.

In the case of the *Palapa B-2* and *Westar VI* satellites, it was later established that the failure to complete this sequence of events satisfactorily had resulted from the PAM-D's solid propellant motor cutting-out prematurely, probably through unscheduled separation of the rocket motor's exhaust nozzle. Consequently, the satellites remained in their unusable, low-Earth orbits which tracking stations around the world were unable to cope with. Although radio contact was established with both satellites soon after the failure, it was realised that the problem could not be resolved by using the on-board apogee motors because they had insufficient power to raise the craft orbits to the extent required. There was no choice other than to abandon the satellites altogether or attempt their salvage.

The latter option offered the opportunity to save face and recoup much of the insurance money paid-out. Urged on by the insurance companies, the salvage option was decided on and NASA set about designing the equipment and procedures with which to effect safe recovery.

In fact, the origins of space salvage can be traced back to 1973 when Charles Conrad and Joseph Kerwin were compelled to assume the role of mechanics to save their orbiting space station Skylab when malfunctioning solar panels threatened its survival.

More recently, in April 1984, the failed Solar Maximum Mission (*Solarmax*) satellite provided an opportunity to effect an in-orbit repair during shuttle mission 41-C. Some of the equipment required for the

(left): Pre-flight training with the apogee kick motor capture device prior to the launch of shuttle mission 51-A. NASA

(below): Astronaut Dale A. Gardner approaching the Westar VI satellite over the Bahamas Banks in readiness for the capture. The end of the Remote Manipulator System can be seen on the right. NASA

71

later, even more complex, operation to recover the *Palapa B-2* and *Westar VI* satellites was used for the *Solarmax* repair, which provided an ideal opportunity to test it in working conditions.

Challenger, which was also the shuttle vehicle for mission 41-C, was manoeuvred into position about 61 metres (200 feet) from *Solarmax* on 9 April 1984. A capture tool, known as the Trunnion Pin Acquisition Device (TPAD), was then fixed to the arms of a Manned Manoeuvring Unit (MMU), a self-propelled free-flight back pack. Astronaut George D. Nelson then flew out to the *Solarmax* with the MMU where he attempted to clamp the TPAD onto a protruding pin on the satellite. This failed to lock, however, and two further attempts to connect were equally unsuccessful. At this point, the procedure had to be abandoned because tumbling motions in the satellite, induced by the docking attempts, also prevented all efforts to grapple it directly by the Remote Manipulator System (RMS) or Canadarm, a jointed winch or crane device which was to feature prominently in the later satellite salvage operation.

During the following night, the mission's Operations Controllers at the Goddard Space Flight Center re-established control over the *Solarmax*. By using its back-up system of magnetic torquing bars they were able to stabilise it and reduce its movements until they had become only a slow, regular spin.

On the morning of 10 April, the satellite was successfully captured by the RMS at the first attempt and transferred into Challenger's cargo bay. There it was locked in a special cradle while Astronaut Nelson and his colleague, James D. van Hoften, carried out the repairs. These involved the replacement of a faulty Altitude Control Motor (ACM) and a main electronics box for a polarimeter instrument.

The *Solarmax* satellite was released into orbit the next day and, after thirty days of monitoring by the Operations Center, it was given a clean bill of health, permitting measurement of the sun's total energy output to be resumed. The savings resulting from repairing this scientific satellite, compared with the cost of building and launching a new one, amounted to many millions of dollars. As a precursor to the more intricate satellite salvage planned for later that year, it provided a wealth of valuable experience and was an unqualified success.

Recovery of the *Palapa* and *Westar* craft was scheduled to be carried out on shuttle mission 51-A, planned for November 1984, so pre-flight training and preparation was commenced in earnest. In addition to the regular, two-man shuttle flight crew, three specialists were attached to the team with the satellite salvage activity specifically in mind. They were Joseph P. Allen, PhD, Dale A. Gardner, Commander USN, and Mrs Anna L. Fisher, MD, the first mother to go into space, who had been closely involved in the further development and pre-flight testing of the special, extending, articulated winch, which was a particularly vital piece of equipment if the satellite salvage was to be successfully undertaken on this occasion.

The other crew members were Frederick H. Hauck, Captain USN, the Commander of shuttle mission 51-A, and David M. Walker, Commander USN, the shuttle pilot, an interesting case of reversal of normal rank seniority.

Mission 51-A was to be the second scheduled flight for the space shuttle *Discovery*. Apart from the satellite recovery operation, two new satellites, *Anik D2* (Telesat H) and *Leasat 1* (Syncom IV-1), would be deployed. A number of other experiments requiring weightless or non-atmospheric conditions would also be performed. The deployments would take place first in order to vacate fully the shuttle cargo hold and provide adequate working space for manoeuvring the recovered satellites during the stowage phase.

The technique for recovering *Westar VI* and *Palapa B-2* was essentially the same in each case, comprising five stages:

1.   Location and capture of the satellite - first remotely and then by the orbiter's robot winch arm.

2.   Pre-stowage removal of projections and attachment of Manoeuvring/berthing adaptors.

73

3.   Manoeuvring of the satellite pre-stowage.

4.   Berthing of the satellite in the shuttle payload bay.

5.   Removal and stowage of recovery adaptors.

These stages were rehearsed constantly throughout the programme of pre-sortie training, and operation of the specially designed tools and equipment was practised in simulated weightless conditions. By the programmed launch day, 7 November 1984, the crew members of shuttle *Discovery* were more than ready to undertake the tasks that lay ahead of them.

The launch of the *Discovery* had to be made between 7 and 11 November to ensure that the shuttle was inserted into the same orbital plane as the satellites to be retrieved, as well as in a period which would both permit rendezvous with the satellites to be accomplished and provide the most suitable deployment opportunities for the new spacecraft. Delay of the launch beyond 11 November would have meant a postponement of 45 days until the next occasion when ideal circumstances for all the mission's tasks again coincided.

In the event, this was unneccessary as there was no lengthy delay.

The launch of shuttle mission 51-A took place at 8.18am (Eastern Standard Time) on 8 November 1984. The duration of the mission was programmed for nine days with retrieval of *Palapa B-2* on day five (12 November) and recovery of *Westar VI* two days later (14 November).

Four days after launch, on 11 November, having satisfactorily completed the deployments and other experiments, space shuttle *Discovery* was gradually manoeuvred into the same orbital plane as *Palapa B-2* in readiness for the start of the first salvage operation, the following morning. The positions of both satellites had been adjusted previously, using their onboard attitude adjustment systems. This had placed them into near identical 335 by 355 kilometre high (205 by 220 mile high) parking orbits, approximately 1,125 kilometres (700 miles) apart. Simultaneously, their rates of rotation were reduced to about 1 rpm.

The following day, final rendezvous attunements were made, bringing the orbiting vehicle to within 15.25 metres (50 feet) of *Palapa B-2* at the closest point of approach. Once the orbiting speeds and relative positions of the two craft had been fully synchronised, mission specialists Allen, Fisher and Gardner left the space shuttle to begin the physical work of the first of the two retrievals.

The task commenced with Allen donning his Manned Manoeuvring Unit (MMU), and flying over, untethered, to the *Palapa B-2* satellite with a specially constructed Apogee Kick Motor Capture Device (ACD). This looked rather like a combination of the probe and drogue-like attachments employed in in-flight refuelling operations to assist positive docking between aircraft. As soon as he was stabilised at the bottom end of the rogue satellite, Allen inserted the 1.8 metre (6 foot) long instrument into the spent apogee kick motor casing, inside the aft skirt of *Palapa B-2*. Once locked into place, Allen was able to employ his MMU jets to arrest the remaining rotation of the satellite, using special brake pads on the capture device.

This complete, the astronaut salvor was then able safely to move the satellite closer to the orbiting vehicle where Anna Fisher was waiting to extend the articulated Remote Manipulator System (RMS) to capture a grappling fixture mounted on the side of the ACD, in order to secure the satellite. During launch and re-entry, the Canadian-built Remote Manipulator System, probably the most essential piece of equipment available to the recovery team, was stowed in an extended position, along the side of the shuttle's cargo bay.

Operated by Anna Fisher throughout this critical phase, connection of the RMS with the Apogee Capture Device was eventually concluded satisfactorily but not before Joseph Allen had spent 90 minutes acting as the securing link to the satellite when hitches were experienced during the grappling manoeuvre. The satellite was then lowered into the shuttle cargo bay where Dale Gardner, the third of the mission's three specialists,

was stationed alongside a special support pallet in readiness to prepare the satellite for stowage.

After the launch of *Palapa B-2*, the previous February, an omni-directional antenna had been remotely extended from the satellite. It was now necessary to remove this antenna to allow the satellite to fit into its waiting pallet. It was also necessary for the astronaut to attach a bridge structure or A-frame to the top, unsecured end of *Palapa B-2* because the satellite had to be re-orientated for vertical stowage. After this was finished, the RMS grasp on the satellite was transferred to the end with the bridge structure. Allen was then cleared to undock the Apogee Kick Motor Capture Device and restow this and his Manned Manoeuvring Unit aboard the *Discovery*.

All that now remained to be done to complete the retrieval operation was for Fisher to lower the satellite into the shuttle, top end up, in position on its pallet in the middle of the payload bay. Secured in position there, Gardner and Allen then removed the A-frame bridge structure that had been fitted earlier, so that the cargo bay doors could be closed in readiness for the return to Earth. After some six hours' work, the recovery operation was finally complete!

Technically precise in all respects, the difficult salvage of the *Palapa B-2* satellite had been executed with surgical precision, giving an impression of simplicity that belied the complexity of the exercise and the acute dangers to which the astronauts had been exposed. *Palapa B-2*, and the *Westar VI*, weighed around 575 kilograms apiece. Each was hurtling around the Earth at 32,400 kilometres per hour (17,500 miles per hour). So too were the astronauts themselves though, relative to the spacecraft, they were stationary. If ever there was an instance in which the full value of careful advanced planning was both needed and demonstrated, this had been it.

When, two days later, *Discovery* rendezvoused with the *Westar VI* satellite, the entire retrieval procedure was repeated in every detail, the only difference being that Gardner and Allen reversed their roles on this occasion. This was presumably to give more than one astronaut practical experience of a wide range of the manoeuvres involved in the salvage operation. The grappling phase, which had run into problems with *Palapa B-2*, went considerably more smoothly in the case of the *Westar VI*. As if to understate this, a lighter note was introduced to the proceedings at this point. Throughout the two salvage operations, photographs had been taken of each stage for evaluation purposes and for release to the world's press and television news organisations. Just as the recaptured *Westar VI* was being lowered into the shuttle's cargo bay, Dale Gardner cheekily produced a "For Sale" sign with which he posed for the camera.

The space shuttle *Discovery* landed at the Kennedy Space Center on 15 November bringing to a momentous end the first successful salvage of equipment from space, its crew no doubt more than satisfied with a job well done.

Back in London, the Lutine Bell had been rung at Lloyds to announce the successful recovery of the two satellites, possibly the first occasion that this had occurred for a non-marine prize and certainly the first time for recoveries from space. Later, astronauts Dale Gardner and Joseph Allen were awarded the Lloyd's Silver Medal for meritorious service, another unique distinction.

Realistically, though, with dependence on so much specialised equipment, designed with the *Palapa B-2* and *Westar VI* satellites almost exclusively in mind, this operation had been a far cry from the kind of multi-capability, commercial salvage undertaken at sea by companies like Smit and Wijsmuller.

Equally, though, the growth of the commercial space industry and the establishment of permanent space stations, such as the proposed Columbus, will necessitate the development of both space salvage techniques and construction skills. In that context, when looking back in the future, after another twenty five years of progress, the achievements of the crew of shuttle *Discovery* on mission 51-A will be seen to rank, in the chronology of space salvage, alongside Yuri Gagarin's flight in April 1961, in the chronology of space flight.

A postscript to the 1984 space salvage serves to demonstrate the extent of progress that has been made since that time in the recovery of objects from this most challenging of environments.

In January 1990 the largest object yet was successfully captured in space and returned to Earth for repairs. This was the bus-sized Long Duration Exposure Facility (LDEF) which had been first launched in 1984 and which had been originally scheduled for recovery during the autumn of 1986. These plans had to be revised in the wake of the loss of the space shuttle *Challenger* in January 1986, after which all space shuttle launches were suspended until September 1988.

On 12 January, following a million mile chase around the globe, the space shuttle *Columbia* (Mission STS-32) was finally able to secure the huge, out-of-control satellite using a giant robot arm. Commander Dan Brandenstein manoeuvred his shuttle vehicle alongside the laboratory satellite, some 320 kilometres (220 miles) above the Pacific Ocean, as both craft orbited the Earth at a speed of 32,400 kilometres per hour (17,500 miles per hour).

Then, flying in formation, the shuttle astronauts extended the robot arm to grapple the satellite. After a four-hour photographic session the captive LDEF was loaded into the *Columbia's* payload bay for return to Earth where it arrived on 20 January 1990.

NASA plans next to construct the permanently orbiting space station Columbus, some 480 kilometres (300 miles) out in space, to serve as a repair and servicing station for all satellites, eliminating the need for

the costly operation of returning them to Earth for repair and subsequent re-launch. Manned by scientists and technicians, it is hoped that this will be in place by the mid-1990's.

A further postscript completes the story of the two satellites recovered in November 1984, confirming the value of the salvage exercise. On 7 April 1990 the refurbished *Westar VI* satellite, re-designed *Asiasat,* was replaced in orbit, launched aboard a Chinese 'Long March' space vehicle. Just 6 days later, the similarly repaired and overhauled *Palapa B-2,* now re-designated *Palala B-2R* was launched into orbit for the second time on the Interim Delta II rocket booster 6925 from Pad 17, Cape Canaveral. Both satellites are now functioning fully and satisfactorily.

(left): The Westar VI *satellite, top right, being lowered towards the shuttle cargo bay. Astronaut Dale Gardner's Manned Manoeuvering Unit can be clearly seen in this picture.* NASA

(below): Following stowage of Westar VI, *astronaut Dale Gardner, left, holds up a 'For Sale' sign, making light reference to the status of the salvaged communications satellite.* NASA

77

Like a Beached Whale

The Japanese attack on Pearl Harbor in December 1941 released a rush of unbridled enthusiasm to demonstrate America's commitment to the overthrow of the totalitarian powers of Europe and Asia, after long years of awkward neutrality. This was no less true of official organisations than of ordinary citizens and in those first few months of hostilities, the character of much of America's war preparations was frenzied and ill-planned. The Navy Department was as guilty as any other of the armed services and as the solution to America's chronic shortage of transports lay in the seizure of Axis and Vichy vessels caught up in her ports, the stage was set for the French Atlantic record breaker Normandie to become an expensive victim of this ill-guided fervour.

Conversion work on the great liner commenced on 24 December 1941 with the target date for completion set, incredibly, at 1 February 1942.

Resulting from this, a combination of badly organised conversion work was carried out simultaneously with the premature stowage of stores and equipment for the ship's maiden troop voyage, bringing highly inflammable life jackets into fatal proximity with unshielded electric arc torches. Worse still, the fire-fighting facilities aboard the vessel were neglected and unmanned, aggravating an already threatening situation. Out of a total of 666 extinguishers, only 10 had been converted to meet American specifications and more than 50% were either in a totally useless condition or only partly filled. Thus it was, with a certain element of inevitability, that the *Normandie* was a blazing inferno by mid-afternoon on 9 February 1942, already belching a funeral pyre over downtown Manhattan.

The confused state of the ship's adaptation for war duties was evident from the illogical sequence of the various tasks that formed part of the conversion programme. Quite apart from the fact that troop equipment was being brought aboard long before work was complete or the ship was ready to sail to Boston for drydocking, there were numerous other signs that outwardly alerted the trained eye to the impending tragedy.

Internally, various groups were working so incoherently that they were almost tripping over each other, and some tradesmen were undoing the work already carried out by others before them. For instance, painters and men laying linoleum floors were working ahead of others who were

78

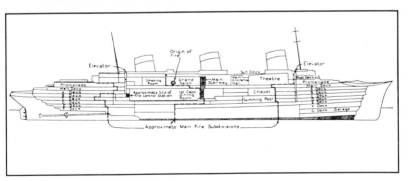

(top): The Lafayette (ex Normandie) *on fire during the afternoon of 9 February 1942. The fatal list, caused by over-zealous fire-fighting, which doomed her to capsize, is already evident.* Associated Press

(above): Side elevation of the Normandie *showing the location of the main vertical bulkheads and the point of origin of the fire.*

tasked to carry out structural alterations in the same areas.

Externally, almost the first work to be carried out was the application of a coat of camouflage paint when painting was normally the last job to be finished. The ship had already been re-named *Lafayette* and the letters of her former name removed even before the replacements were ready for welding into place. So she was, to all intents and purposes, a nameless vessel when she rolled over on to her side in the mud and ice of the Hudson River following the fire-fighting debacle which itself rivalled the conversion for its catastrophic ineptness.

The New York Fire Department, which assumed full and exclusive responsibility for tackling the fire, pursued a single-track solution, in blinkered detachment. This amounted to pouring ever greater volumes of water on to the fire regardless of the consequences to the ship's stability. Proposals to scuttle the ship, to settle her upright on the bottom, a move which would have probably saved her, were rejected out of hand through fears that burning oil might spread the fire to shore installations.

Half-submerged, half-exposed above the surface, the *Lafayette* (ex *Normandie*) looked like some vast beached whale, a monstrous monument to official blundering. The Navy Department was anxious to remove this seemingly unconcealable source of embarrassment but the former liner was the biggest ship yet to settle in this attitude and there was no previous experience in raising vessels of this size available to guide her salvors. The predicament was further complicated by the fact that the hull lay at an angle between two of the finger-like Manhattan piers, leaving little room to manoeuvre, and was resting partly in deep mud and partly in the deeper water of the dredged berth, pivoting on a rocky ledge, as the tide ebbed and flowed.

To its credit, the Navy Department approached the salvage operation in a thoroughly professional manner. Although it was a hugely expensive undertaking, this was in part mitigated by the wise decision to exploit the exercise as a source of training for divers and other salvage personnel. Early on, before the full realisation of the cost of the operation had dawned, the decision was made to attempt to save the ship by raising her with a view to restoration. While this was determined, in part, as a good public relations exercise, to redeem the situation, it was eminently preferable to the only realistic alternative which was to break the vessel up piecemeal where she lay. Either way, it was important to clear the obstructed dock as soon as possible in order to recommission it for urgent war service.

The Navy Department contracted Merritt Chapman & Scott, then the world's largest salvage organisation, to raise the capsized ship. They assigned Captain John Tooker to supervise the work, a highly experienced salvage expert and diver who had cut his teeth working with his father, Captain Israel Tooker, raising the American liner *St Paul* which sank in like fashion and in almost the same place during World War 1. The

(left): Seen from the air, the removal of the Lafayette's superstructure has been completed as 'Normandieville'- the numerous barges and workboats grows to occupy the vacated space. At top left is the Mauretania and to the right is the Queen Elizabeth. US National Archives

(below): Pumping dry is underway in this view of the salvage scene and already the Lafayette has turned through almost 45 degrees. US National Archives

81

method adopted to right this much smaller vessel offered possibilities for the lifting of the *Lafayette* and experience of this earlier operation proved to be invaluable. Maintaining the family link through another generation, three of John Tooker's sons also assisted with the salvage of the *Lafayette*.

Liaison between the salvors and the Bureau of Ships was through Commander William Sullivan, the United States Navy's Salvage Supervisor, while Captain Tooker was further supported by Mr A.C.W. Siecke, Merritt Chapman & Scott's Chief Naval Architect and Marine Engineer.

Preliminary examination of the ship and her situation suggested that, in order to achieve a successful conclusion to the salvage, the operation would have to be undertaken according to the following programme of actions:

1. Remove the ship's superstructure down to the main deck in the hull.

2. Clear away all débris and wreckage surrounding the ship and obstructing the area between Piers 88 and 90.

3. Erect bulkheads at strategic points within the sunken hull to effect a series of watertight compartments.(When the *Lafayette* had turned over on to her beam ends, only a small number of her watertight doors had been closed while many apertures on her port side, the side now resting on the bottom, had been left wide open.)

4. Pump these watertight compartments dry so that the ship's inherent stability would right her.

This simple conception of the stages of the operation was carried out, more-or-less, according to plan. In reality, though, the task was far from straightforward, being fraught with numerous difficulties and dangers and, when it came to the final stage, the process of flotation had to be assisted by mechanical means.

Work started almost immediately on 10 February 1942. A veritable 'shanty town' of floating workshops, dumb barges and other workboats was assembled around the hull from which the process of removing deck fittings and superstructure proceeded in earnest. From airborne news cameras, closely monitoring progress from an uncensored vantage point, it looked like hundreds of termites swarming over a dead elephant.

The most immediate external evidence that the salvage operation was underway was the removal of the ship's funnels, commencing with

82

the forwardmost of the three. Removal of other top hamper, which commenced at about the same time, was not particularly difficult to execute as far as the ship's exposed areas were concerned, but it was a quite different matter when it came to the equivalent submerged portions.

Simultaneously, work commenced on tidying up the inside of the ship, in readiness for sealing openings on the submerged, port side. The *Lafayette* was full of the remnants of the disaster - charred and broken furniture and fittings, heaps of broken glass, the discarded tools, equipment and materials hastily abandoned by the evacuated conversion force, bundles of dislodged carpeting, piping, electric cable and an assortment of other junk. Within compartments that were below water level, all this mess was enshrouded by an icy black slime of near-freezing water and oil. As far as possible, within the time constraints, this had to be cleared in order to render the spaces inside the ship safer for divers to work in.

Working within the ship was already enough of a nightmare anyway, with surfaces rotated, presenting divers with an incongruous maze.

Deckheads and decks had become bulkheads and vice versa, stairs and ladders ran horizontally and companionways, which had to be negotiated along their sides, were canted at crazy angles. Through open doorways gaped treacherous pits of blackness. There was a total lack of light such that the dense darkness was like that inside an unlit mine shaft. It was quite literally impossible for divers to see their hands in front of their faces.

In spite of these extremely unpleasant and dangerous conditions, this internal débris was gradually removed and loaded on barges for conveyance to a landfill site. The weight of each barge-load was estimated and recorded, as was all the steelwork and other material removed from the vessel's superstructure.

This information was of vital importance to the salvage specialists, permitting them to calculate the changing position of the ship's centre of gravity. When afloat, the stability of a vessel is governed, in very simple terms, by the relationship of its centre of buoyancy to its centre of gravity. Critical to this is the position of the centre of gravity relative to the metacentre, the point of intersection of a vertical line through a changed centre of buoyancy, such as when the vessel is heeled over, and a line projected from top to bottom through the centre of a transverse section of the ship. For as long as the centre of gravity lies below the metacentre, the ship will remain stable, irrespective of the degree of roll, but once the centre of gravity rises above the metacentre, the ship is in an unstable condition and is likely to capsize. Salvors who take advantage of a ship's natural stability to assist in righting it, as John Tooker planned to do with the *Lafayette*, are in effect exploiting this important principle by contriving to return the centre of gravity to a point below the metacentre.

Outside the ship, beneath the water, the working conditions were equally appalling. In the early stages of the salvage operation, the hull was still enshrouded within the ice of the harsh New York winter while a cocktail of deep mud and untreated sewage presented another alarming hazard. Divers working on the vessel's port side were often smothered from head to foot in this thick ooze making it difficult, if not impossible, for them to move and, in the very poor light, it was quite easy for them to lose their bearings.

Progress on stripping the *Lafayette's* superstructure down to her main deck was good and by mid-May everything above water level had been cleared down to the promenade deck, in spite of interruptions caused by outbreaks of fire. Throughout this period, during which workmen were particularly active in the use of cutting gear, fires were a constant menace. There were one or two quite serious fires but now at least the authorities were adequately prepared for the likelihood, having provided, in a classic example of closing the stable door after the horse has bolted, well-manned and well-trained fire crews who promptly and efficiently dealt with each incident.

Below water the situation was somewhat less well advanced and many of the fixtures and much of bulkhead plating on the extreme port side was left in place to be removed progressively as it was exposed above the surface during the refloating operation.

Also, during May, a 91.5 metre (300 foot) section of the seamost end of Pier 88 was demolished as the *Lafayette's* stern end was lying partly against the pier's piles. There were fears that complications would arise during the righting phase of the operation if the ship jammed-up against the pier's sub-structure while being rotated into an upright position.

By the end of May workmen had completed the erection of scaffolding over the exposed hull in readiness for future stages of the salvage operation. At about this time, plans were announced for the possible reconstruction of the wrecked ship as an aircraft carrier after she had been refloated. It might be assumed that such a suggestion was a further example of efforts on the part of the Navy Department's PR people to play down the gravity of the initial carelessness in the conversion of the *Normandie* to a troopship, by demonstrating a positive attitude concerning her future naval employment and implying, simultaneously, that such a major surgical exercise on the ship would have been necessary anyway. The fact was that this was a serious proposal resulting from an evaluation exercise funded by the Navy Department and undertaken by the highly regarded firm of naval architects, Gibbs & Cox. The exercise had been commissioned by a largely civilian committee, which had been appointed by the Secretary of the Navy on 15 April 1942, tasked to decide finally whether scrapping or reconstruction was the best course of action following salvage.

CHAPTER 6

This planned conversion of the ex-*Normandie* has been the subject of debate since World War 2, invariably presented as only a vague notion, because of the ship's inherent unsuitability for such employment, rather than as a matter of serious engineering intent. It should be remembered that, at that time, the unsuitability of such thin-skinned vessels for carrier conversion had not been fully appreciated in naval circles. Besides, the urgent need for carriers rather outweighed reservations over scantling strength. Elsewhere, similar proposals for conversion of the *Queen Elizabeth*, *Rex* and *Europa* were also the subject of feasibility studies. In the event, the reason why the *Lafayette* ex *Normandie* was not rebuilt as an aircraft carrier was not so much due to her lack of hull strength but, rather, because the Navy Department considered it had already spent enough money on salvaging the ship, while the question of an urgent need for aircraft carriers no longer applied once purpose-built 'Essex' class fleet carriers began leaving the shipyards in increasing numbers.

The preparations for righting the *Lafayette*, through the elimination of top hamper and the clearance of débris from inside the ship and from the surrounding water were progressing well. The pumping out operation to restore the ship's buoyancy was scheduled to commence in late summer of 1942. However, before this could be started, the *Lafayette* had to be made watertight. In accomplishing this, the salvage team was confronted by an obstacle of some magnitude which unavoidably slowed down the pace of the salvage operation - this was the patching over of the profusion of apertures, holes and punctures distributed about the ship's hull.

Numerous portholes on both sides, which had been left open, now had to be sealed tight. Besides these, there were up to 4,500 other openings to close over, including 16 cargo ports, up to 16.5 metres by 6.7 metres (54 feet by 22 feet) in size, the many doors and other entrances to the hull and a myriad of minor apertures, some of them only a few hundred square centimetres in area. There was also a series of holes low on the starboard side that had been cut by Navy men, during the firefighting operation, in a vain bid to counterflood four ballast tanks to arrest the ship's list.

Sealing the submerged, port side portholes presented a major challenge. Divers had systematically to investigate each cabin, room or other edge space on that side of the ship for absolute water security to be assured. Each porthole was located by groping towards it, using touch and the memory of a pre-sortie study of models and plans as a guide, and then excavating any amount of thick mud or silt that blocked access to the point of interest.

An ingenious device was contrived by Captain Tooker to effect a dependable seal to each open porthole, a simple but clever invention which was destined to be one of the more important legacies of the

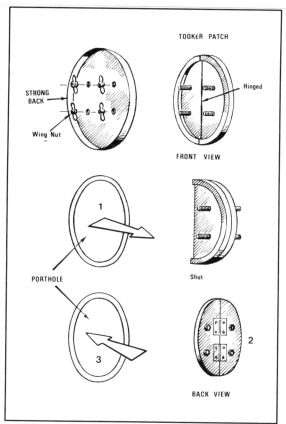

TOOKER PATCH

STRONG BACK

Wing Nut

FRONT VIEW

Hinged

PORTHOLE

Shut

BACK VIEW

1

2

3

(left): The Tooker's Patch used to seal the open portholes of the USS Lafayette, *showing its method of operation.*

(below): The Lafayette *upright and afloat at the Todd Shipyard's Brooklyn Pier. At this time no decision had been made on her future and many hoped that she would survive.*
World Ship Photo Library

86

Lafayette salvage. Known as a "Tooker's Patch", after its originator, it comprised a 7.5 centimetre (3 inch) thick wooden disc, with a diameter somewhat greater than the porthole aperture, cut in half centrally and hinged together with heavy-duty door hinges. Around its perimeter, on one side, a 0.625 centimetre (quarter inch) rubber gasket was attached. Finally, four long toggle bolts, two to each half, were fitted through the patch with their threaded ends projecting on the same side as the rubber seal. Armed with one of these, the diver folded it double to insert it through the porthole. On the far side it was opened-out flat and drawn back against the outside surface of the porthole's brass rim.

A strong back, with holes that lined up with four bolts, was then fitted on the inside and the whole arrangement tightened up with nuts. Any amount of pressure outside the vessel, as water was pumped out of the ship, only served to achieve an even tighter seal.

In all 356 "Tooker's Patches" were fitted, some taking as long as a week to get into place. This is hardly surprising, considering that each porthole had first to be located and exposed by the diver, by which time he was often already thoroughly exhausted. Assuming he had enough energy left to carry on, he then had to assemble the mechanism in near or total darkness, manipulating the fiddly components with thick diver's gloves that denied all sensitivity of touch.

The bigger holes in the *Lafayette*'s sides were patched over with panels constructed from a frame of steel girders overlaid with thick wooden planks and edged off with strips of rubber that were removed from the ship's decks. The "Tooker's Patches" and all the other seals were fabricated in the workshops built on barges alongside the wreck or erected along the exposed sides of the sunken hull, all of which had by now acquired the rather flippant nick-name 'Normandieville'.

Meanwhile, as the sealing work proceeded, watertight bulkheads were being constructed throughout the ship to compartment it in readiness for controlled pumping. Simultaneously, the decks were shored-up to withstand the pressures to which they would be subjected during this phase of the salvage operation, a task that consumed over a mile-and-a-half of shoring timber.

The watertight bulkheads were fabricated of immense wooden beams bolted together in juxtaposed, overlapping layers, a configuration rather like that employed in the construction of wooden yachts' hulls, and sealed around the corners and edges with pockets filled with concrete.

Not surprisingly, all this pre-lift preparation work took a considerable amount of time. Although the installation of pumps commenced in November 1942, it was not until the following August that they were tested in readiness for the start of pumping the *Lafayette* dry.

Some 98 pumps in total, capable of pumping ten million kilograms (10,000 tons) of water an hour, were lifted aboard the ship and strategically located. Each pump was fixed to a platform which was hinged at the end towards the troopship's upper deck levels. This permitted the incline of the pumps to be adjusted relative to the ship as it turned into an upright position. By the means of this simple device it was possible to keep them within 15 degrees of horizontal, maintaining maximum pumping efficiency. It was also necessary, occasionally, to reposition the pumps during the righting operation in order to keep them as near to the water level as possible.

Pumping commenced in earnest on 4 August 1943. In that first day the water inside the hull was reduced by 2.75 metres (9 feet), at which point the distance from the ship's stem to the water was some 2.5 metres (8 feet). An indicator rod, calibrated in feet, had been fixed vertically from the *Lafayette's* prow, extending down into the water, with which the gradual increase in this dimension could be measured as the righting manoeuvre proceeded.

When the *Lafayette* had capsized, she had come to rest at an angle of 79 degrees from the vertical. By 7 August 1943, just three days after pumping out began, the incline of the ship had been reduced to 67 degrees while the height of her stem above the water had increased to 6.0 metres (20 feet).

At this time there was concern that the remaining plating of the promenade deck on the port side, which had been inaccessible to divers for cutting away, would now act like a vast paddle causing resistance to the righting momentum. Further, there was even a fear that the weight of water being supported by this obstacle might tear the plating away to leave a gaping, unpluggable cavity in her side, instantly rendering the entire operation a failure. Luckily, this was not the case and three days later again, when the port side promenade deck was sufficiently clear of the surface, workmen proceeded to cut away this metalwork, as well as the port side davits. Presumably, this was a contingency move in case, for any reason, the operation had to be temporarily reversed.

By now, the ship was inclined at 42 degrees and the distance from the bow to the water had reached 11.75 metres (38.5 feet). Captain Tooker forecast that the operation would take only six more weeks to complete, a brave prediction, even coming from this expert, given the size of the ship being salvaged and the fact that, historically, salvage is an unpredictable business in which the unexpected is frequently encountered.

So it was with the *Lafayette*. Almost as Tooker's announcement was being broadcast by the news media, his team hit major snags. Serious leaks, pinpointed by divers as being in compartment 16, were encountered as early as 11 August. All available pumps in the area were working flat out but they were making little impression on the water level which, if anything, was actually rising. It seems that the initial righting movement to the hull had disturbed massive ruptures in this section which had, until that point, been undetected by the underwater teams responsible for sealing the ship.

CHAPTER 6

In a bid to staunch the flood of water, divers deposited vast amounts of waste rag, oakum and mattresses, that were no longer required for troop use, into the sea in the vicinity of the affected compartment, driving it all under the hull plating hopefully to be carried by the suction into the holes, to clog them up. But this was all, unfortunately, to no avail and, from this point, the final phase of the salvage was overshadowed by the relentless battle to overcome the leaks in the weakened compartment. Ultimately, of course, success depended on winning this battle.

Over the next month pumping effort was steadily increased so that the water level in compartment 16 could be kept, as near as possible, synchronised with that in the adjacent compartments in order to minimise strain on the separating bulkheads. The only practical solution to plugging the ruptures proved to be concrete, in liberal quantities.

First, a patch was laid in the curve of the bilge between 13 and 16 August. This held for two days, allowing pumping to be temporarily resumed at nearly full scale. A brief interlude that followed to permit consideration of alternative courses of action served to confirm that the use of concrete was, in reality, the only practical option available. Consequently, concrete pouring on a truly grand scale recommenced in compartment 16 on 7 September. Hundreds of tons later and with the pumps increased to thirteen, the salvage team was able to contain the problem sufficiently well to permit the resumption of the righting operation on 12 September. By the end of that day the *Lafayette* had turned to an angle of 45 degrees.

The following day, electric beach gear winches on shore were activated to drag the ship's stern away from Pier 88 in preparation for refloating. Over two days, the *Lafayette* was moved sixteen feet up river. Earlier, these winches had been connected to the vessel with wires on 6 August as a contingency to reduce lateral stress across the promenade deck.

With pumping-out continuing in compartment 16, the salvage team was able to proceed to its ultimate goal but when it was finally achieved it was announced in such a muted and restrained fashion that it came as something of an anti-climax. This was on the night of 15/16 September 1943 when, for the first time since she capsized, the *Lafayette* floated completely independently. Her buoyancy had been initially restored two days earlier but only at high water. As the tide ebbed she had settled once more on the bottom.

This magnificent achievement, modestly acclaimed as it may have been, culminated what remains to this day the greatest salvage operation ever successfully executed. The *Lafayette* is the largest vessel ever to be refloated and for many years the exercise was also the most expensive. Shortly after its conclusion the United States Navy disclosed that it had cost $4.5 million to complete (£18 million by then contemporary rates of exchange or allowing for 45 years of inflation and currency devaluation, some £150 million).

Following refloating, the *Lafayette* was prepared for handing back to the United States Navy. The hull was secured, with the leaks to compartment 16 fully patched. When handed over on 27 October 1943 she was almost on an even keel, the slight list having been deliberately contrived so that water from residual leaks would gather in places where it could be conveniently pumped away.

Redesignated APV-4, the *Lafayette* was towed to the Navy drydock at Bayonne, New Jersey for comprehensive hull repairs on 3 November 1943. In effect, by this time, she was nothing more than a huge floating hulk, all interior material having been removed from her, including the deck shoring timbers. Four months later, her hull fully intact and with the hint of fresh paint along her waterline, she was moved to the Todd Shipyards' Brooklyn pier at Columbia Street, near to the entrance to the Gowanus Canal. She lingered there for another twenty months, awaiting a decision on her future.

Then, on 20 September 1945, the United States Navy declared her to be surplus to their requirements. The *Lafayette* was consequently struck from the Navy List on 11 October of that year and transferred to Maritime Commission custody until 3 October 1946 when she was finally sold to Lipsett Incorporated for scrapping at Port Newark, New Jersey.

This final, fateful decision confirmed that no attempt would be made to derive some lasting benefit from the hull that had consumed so much time, effort and money by restoring it to a re-employable condition.

Negative though this was, for immediately after World War 2 commercial shipping of all types was in critically short supply, the disposal of the *Lafayette* did not mean that her salvage had been altogether an extremely expensive waste of time. Quite apart from the fact that the vital berthing facilities at two of the West 49th Street piers had been restored for shipping movements, with little further disruption to the pier structures, much valuable knowledge and experience had been gained from the exercise which was to benefit generations of future United States Navy divers and salvage technicians, equipping them with the expertise to deal with whatever recovery requirements the service was likely to encounter.

CHAPTER 7

From the Ocean's Depths

Possibly the most bizarre salvage exercise to take place over the last 25 years occurred during the summer of 1974 when agents of the CIA, US Navy salvage personnel and representatives of a number of major American corporations were involved in a bid to raise a foundered Soviet submarine from the sea-bed of the Pacific Ocean, at one of its deepest points, under a cloak of secrecy.

The story behind the search for this Russian vessel and its attempted recovery was like some fantastic episode from a James Bond novel. Secret appropriations, to fund the operation, were transferred to commercial concerns apparently engaged on an innocent mineral exploration venture. Russian-speaking deep sea divers were hired, specialist ships and equipment assembled and fantastic remunerations paid to participants of the clandestine operation, or so it was claimed. All in all, fact and fiction, it added to the cloak and dagger character of the whole affair, conducted at a time when cold war tensions were still very much at a peak.

At the time, the entire operation, called project 'Jennifer' but also known as project 'Azorian', was shrouded in complete secrecy but some seven years later, after newspapers had pieced together parts of the intriguing jigsaw, most of the details were publicly disclosed. It then became evident that, for a salvage attempt utilising a bathyscaphe, it had been made at the greatest depth ever.

It all began during early March 1968 when a diesel powered Russian 'Golf' class submarine sank in the Pacific, approximately 1,200 kilometres (750 miles) north west of Hawaii, following an explosion suspected to have resulted from a venting mishap when she was blowing her ballast tanks.

The whole incident was closely followed by the US Naval authorities using top secret, super-sensitive underwater listening devices. They had routinely followed the submarine's movements from the moment it left its base in Vladivostok right up to the point when the mortally crippled vessel, suffering its final agonies, sank straight to the bottom, over 4.8 kilometres (3 miles) down, taking its entire complement of men with it.

Between March and May of that year the Soviet Navy made repeated attempts to find the stricken submarine, transmitting everything from coded signals on military frequencies to unciphered, spoken

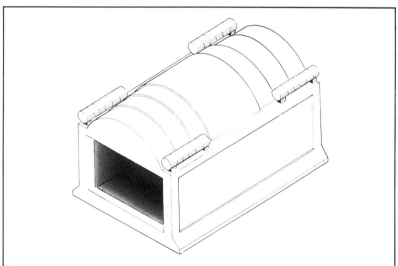

(top): Trieste II *out of the water in November 1979, following modifications.* US Navy

(above): The huge submersible dumb barge NMS-1 which was used to recover part of the salvaged 'Golf' class submarine. Photographs of the barge exist but are the subject of strict security constraints.

messages over the routine marine radio distress channels. Numerous surface vessels were also sent to the ship's last known position to scour the area but all to no avail. Even had they located the vessel it was highly unlikely that it would have been possible for them to retrieve it for it was understood by the American authorities that, at that time, Soviet undersea search and recovery capabilities were markedly inferior to their own.

All this intense activity was also tracked by the US Navy's surveillance specialists, gradually persuading intelligence personnel to conclude that, perhaps, the ill-fated submarine contained much more sophisticated equipment or advanced weaponry than their existing knowledge had suggested. From existing information, intelligence sources were able to reveal that, although ten years old, the casualty had been completely overhauled and modernised, prior to the abortive mission, and had been equipped with nuclear-tipped torpedoes. It was one of a very large class of conventionally-powered submarines operated by the Soviet Navy. The fact that the Russians were, apparently, so intensely anxious to recover the vessel seemed to imply that such urgency was motivated by reasons of concern to preserve the secrecy of something special that may have been installed aboard this particular vessel.

Naturally enough, it followed that whatever it was that the Soviets wanted to keep discreet was of interest to the Americans. Inspired by such reasoning, the Americans started to contemplate a bid to recover the foundered submarine themselves. They had the advantage of a better indication of the position of the accident. Whatever the outcome, it was an ideal opportunity to put their own underwater equipment to the most exacting test and, in so doing, there was a real possibility that they could score a major strategic and intelligence scoop over the Russians.

Initially, before any such attempt to salvage the submarine could be authorised and funded, the intelligence data that had been gathered already had to be validated by a preliminary location of the vessel, followed by surveillance of the wreck to determine its integrity as the basis of formulating a salvage strategy.

Working from all the positioning information derived from electronic fixes on the submarine itself and from observation of Soviet surface craft, co-ordinates were computed and, utilising the bathyscaphe *Trieste II*, the hunt began in earnest in the late 1960s. As if to underline the superiority of American equipment over that available to the Russians, the missing submarine was soon located. The *Trieste II* was manoeuvred down to the sinister grey hull, its deathlike menace amplified by the eeriness and stillness of its dark ocean grave. Already, just by reaching the wreck, the *Trieste II* had created a record of sorts by descending to a depth of 4,880 metres (16,000 feet or approximately 3 miles). When, in September 1985, the submersible camera-craft *Argo* descended to the wreck of the *Titanic*, she was still only operating at a depth of 3,810 metres (12,500 feet).

Once on site, the *Trieste II* proceeded to comprehensively photograph the wrecked 'Golf' class submarine. These pictures revealed that the vessel was still largely intact but that damage from the ballast tank explosions and stress fractures and other weaknesses caused by the extreme pressure, at the depths to which it had plunged, would no doubt cause complications in any bid to raise it in one piece.

After successfully completing the surveillance sortie, high level meetings were held in the Pentagon to decide what the next moves should be. Present were Mr Melvin Laird and Mr David Packard, respectively the US Secretary and Deputy Secretary of Defense in the Nixon administration, along with intelligence officials and military and naval engineering experts.

The photographic evidence was studied and both the technical and military pros and cons of a salvage bid discussed. Clearly, quite apart from the propaganda value that would be derived from accomplishing what the Soviets had been patently incapable of, there were many attractive military trophies to be taken. The US authorities were interested in obtaining the submarine's coding devices and logbooks for their wider intelligence value. Equally, the nuclear-tipped torpedoes with their guidance systems would provide useful clues about the development of both Soviet atomic weaponry and naval ordnance.

94

Also, the hull itself offered the prospect of rich rewards. Though of late 1950s vintage the pressure hull had apparently survived the incredible forces of pressure at this extreme depth. An opportunity to study in detail a design that had this structural strength, as well as an insight into any structural weaknesses or vulnerabilities not immediately obvious, would give tremendous tactical advantages to the Americans. There was also the potential of learning more about Soviet construction techniques, welding methods, propulsion machinery, metallurgic expertise and so on.

Besides all this, there was the remote possibility that the vessel had indeed been fitted with new, experimental equipment, with which the American authorities were not familiar, or had been on a special mission, as hinted at by the Soviets' own intense efforts to locate and recover it.

Those were the potential gains. Against this had to be considered the costs of a salvage exercise. Technically, such a salvage was without precedent and would necessitate the development, at great expense, of much specialised equipment. There was no guarantee of success, either. By this time the Russians had abandoned their efforts to recover the lost undersea craft but there was no way of knowing for certain whether this had been terminated, as suspected, through failure to locate it or instead, through inability to raise it to the surface, though with known technological limitations to their salvage capability the latter was improbable.

All these issues were duly debated and analysed, after which a project plan was submitted to the Pentagon's 40 Committee, its main

strategic planning and project co-ordination body. Approval was saught for the final go-ahead for a salvage operation.

Project 'Jennifer', as it was dubbed, did indeed receive official assent and, because of the security implications, the Central Intelligence Agency (CIA) was assigned the responsibility for the operation through the leadership of Mr Richard Helms.

The CIA co-ordinated the naval and salvage aspects of the operation with the US Navy but elected to recruit the resources of key commercial concerns for the physical recovery. There were two reasons for this. Primarily, it was because these bodies had more sophisticated heavy lift equipment than the Navy. Also, their involvement, under the subterfuge of a mineral prospecting exercise would give the operation the requisite innocent cover that was essential if the recovery was to be effected with all due discretion, free from the glare of unwanted publicity.

Beginning in January 1970, when the project received its official endorsement, various contractors were approached, sworn to secrecy and recruited to the team. Among those engaged were the Hughes Tool Corporation, owned by Howard Hughes and latterly known as the Summa Corporation, as well as the ocean mining divisions of Lockhead, Kennecott, Tenneco and Global Marine, yet another Hughes company.

The recovery plan was based on the interactive utilisation of three key salvage craft. First, there was Global Marine's new ocean recovery and exploration vessel *Glomar Explorer*. Measuring some 27,455 tons gross and 188.6 metres (619 feet) in overall length, she was built at the Sun Shipbuilding & Drydock Company shipyard at Chester, Pennsylvania in 1973. She was now drydocked for modification and for the installation of equipment especially commissioned for project 'Jennifer. To complete the deception, by emphasising her apparent involvement in a deep sea mining operation, specifically a search for manganese nodules located on the sea floor, she was fitted with two retractable drilling towers.

To work in conjunction with the *Glomar Explorer* was a vast, floodable dumb barge designated NMS-1. Registered in Redwood City, California, this immense craft, measuring in the order of 152.5 metres (500 feet) by 45.5 metres (150 feet) resembled a floating drydock cradling a huge cylinder whose diameter was equal to the overall dimension between the two side walls. The high slab-like side structures housed the vessel's pumps, valves, and power generation facilities, also its anchor handling and mooring gear. The central, cylindrical part of the barge was fitted with door mechanisms at either end, permitting it to be completely sealed. The whole structure could be flooded and totally submerged so that large objects, raised from the sea-bed, could be moved into it beneath the surface. Then, when secured in place, the water could be pumped out to raise the craft and its contents above sea level.

For the operation to retrieve the Russian submarine, the barge had fitted beneath it a massive, compound claw device, weighing some

610,000 kilograms (600 tons), which was connected to a shrouded cable. This contained the computerised control links, by which it was operated, and permitted it to be lowered as far as the sea bottom where the Russian submarine lay. Attached to the main claw were another eight subsidiary claw-like devices each of which could be deployed to reinforce the attachment to the entire salvaged object once the main claw had been secured.

The intention was that the barge would be submerged and positioned, at a depth of 45.5 metres (150 feet), immediately beneath the *Glomar Explorer*. From this position, the huge claw would be lowered and, under guidance, secured to the Soviet submarine. Supported by the full complement of securing devices, the submarine would then be raised to the level of the barge where, assisted by other recovery vessels, it would be manoeuvred inside and finally brought to the surface.

The third, vital item of equipment to be utilised for project 'Jennifer' was the bathyscaphe *Trieste II* which was to be employed to assist with all the underwater phases of the operation - surveying the scene, supervising and guiding activities conducted from the surface.

In addition to the three main players, a small flotilla of support craft was required including various work boats as well as tugs to tow the dumb barge into position. The *Glomar Explorer* was to serve as the command centre and accommodation vessel for the duration.

Assembling and commissioning all the necessary equipment for project 'Jennifer' took some considerable time as did the recruitment of suitable, security-safe personnel. The latter involved vetting people's backgrounds, arranging their security clearance and conducting pre-exercise briefings. For this venture, technical competence alone was insufficient.

By the summer of 1974, when everything was ready for the recovery operation to commence, more than 4,000 persons were involved. At this point the Pentagon had estimated the cost of the project at $350 million (£175 million at then contemporary exchange rates).

Two years earlier, on 20 May 1972, it was revealed that the *Trieste II* under the command of Lt. Cdr. Melvyn Bartels USN, had successfully recovered an 'electronic package' from the seabed 5,030 metres (16,500 feet) down at a point 645 kilometres (400 miles) north of Hawaii. This is the greatest depth ever from which salvage has been successfully achieved. The style of the announcements indicated that the exercise had military overtones but was it connected with the impending project 'Jennifer', perhaps a trial run to prove some of the more critical techniques or pieces of equipment? This was not disclosed, nor could it have been, but with the benefit of hindsight it seems to be more than a coincidence that this exercise, in 1972, also involved the attachment of 'special cables' to the salvaged object.

Project 'Jennifer' proper swung into action on 4 July 1974 (was the

(top): The Hughes Glomar Explorer, *owned by the Howard Hughes company,* Global Marine, *which served as mother ship for Project 'Jennifer'.* US Navy

(above): In this view of the Glomar Explorer, *her name now shortened, the central, retractable rig structure is elevated.* Global Marine

date - US Independence Day - another coincidence?) when the *Glomar Explorer*, its accompanying barge NMS-1 and the other support craft arrived over the wreck site in mid Pacific. Exactly a month later, on 4 August, the recovery bid commenced.

The barge was flooded and then stationed in position as intended, allowing the lowering of the claw device to start. It took over eight days for it to reach the wreck, even though the cable was being paid out at a rate of 21.5 metres (70 feet) an hour, which is a potent illustration of the great depth from which it was planned to recover the submarine.

Already on station by the wreck was the *Trieste II*, ready to supervise the deployment of the multiple attachment devices to the submarine's hull, once the main claw had reached the same depth. All this was successfully executed, each claw being guided into position by computer control as television cameras aboard the *Trieste II* relayed the progress of each manoeuvre.

Fully supported fore, aft and amidships, the raising of the submarine from the ocean floor then commenced. Initially, as indicated by the information subsequently released, everything went extremely well, given the potential for mishap in this quite unprecedented salvage, but at a depth of 2,135 metres (7,000 feet) the weakened hull of the submarine suddenly collapsed causing a number of the claw devices to shear off under the strain. No longer fully supported, the submarine broke completely into two parts, at a point roughly one third along its length, with the larger section sinking back to the ocean floor.

The hold on the smaller section remained secure, so the lift effort resumed and it was fully raised to the barge, moved inside and, ultimately, brought to the surface as planned. The loss of the vital equipment meant that the team were unable to repeat the operation to retrieve the remainder of the submarine. This would now have to wait for a future attempt after the team had re-equipped itself.

In the meantime, attention was focused on the part that had been salved. Quite apart from any militarily sensitive material that this may have yielded, it contained the remains of the bodies of several Soviet sailors. These were buried with all appropriate solemnity, in a ceremony conducted in Russian and English which ended with the playing of the Soviet and American national anthems.

Thereafter, the recovery operation was terminated and the cluster of salvage craft departed the scene. In the final reckoning it was claimed that $550 million (£275 million) had been expended on project Jennifer, a huge bill for the American taxpayer, with little to show for it - or so it would seem.

Considering that part of the 'Golf' class submarine had been salvaged, project 'Jennifer could be regarded as having been partially successful but whether or not it fully achieved all that Pentagon planners had hoped for will never be known. All the important details are now the

subject of unanswered questions. It is not known for certain whether a second attempt to recover the rest of the submarine was ever made. That aspect of the operation has been kept under the closest of tight security wraps. Yet, in reality, it is not even certain whether the events of the first salvage bid unfolded precisely as described. That is in the very nature of affairs involving espionage agencies.

For seven years after the event the first salvage operation was kept a close secret. This was because, it was said, key targets had not been found and a second recovery was planned. Premature announcements would have prejudiced this. It can only be assumed, therefore, now that much of the substance of project Jennifer has been made public, that a second, successful salvage operation was undertaken between 1974 and 1981 or that the wreck was abandoned altogether without vital objectives ever being accomplished. Equally, the wreck could have been forsaken for other reasons. Either because it was not considered to be worthwhile expending more money on a lost cause or because the American authorities had in fact already found what they were really seeking on the first visit. It is unlikely that we will ever know.

Despite the remaining mystery about the full extent of the recovered material and the lack of any relevations of substance (apart from the fact that the bodies of victims were recovered), project Jennifer can only be regarded as a highly successful operation. That is, from the intelligence point of view. No intelligence agency ever publicly informs its rivals of its achievements, for its principal objective, at all times, is to keep the adversary guessing. But whether any of the perceived benefits represented good value for money is another question.

99

From a salvage point of view, too, regardless of whether all or only part of the submarine was brought to the surface, it had been an unqualified success. The ability to raise very large objects from unprecedented depths to the surface had been demonstrated. New techniques and equipment had been devised which will be destined, inevitably, to find application in the world of commercial salvage. As has so often been the case in the past in all areas of technology, the frontiers of knowledge and experience have been extended by the demands of military expedience. Such progress could not be achieved in circumstances in which it would be totally dependent on purely commercial funding. Cost implications and the market's requirement for guaranteed returns on risk investment continue to dictate against technological development of this calibre of expense in the commercial sector.

Ship Surgery

On 30 August 1981, the Norwegian cruise ship Royal Viking Star arrived at the AG 'Weser' Seebeckwerft shipyard, Bremerhaven for lengthening by the insertion into her hull of a 27.8 metres (91 feet) prefabricated midships section. To achieve this, the vessel was cut completely in half and her bow section floated away from the stern section to permit the new centre structure to be introduced between them. All three sections were then connected together. On completion, on 22 November of that same year, the Royal Viking Star's gross registered tonnage was re-measured at 28,221, an increase of 6,735 gross tons. Her overall length had also increased to 205.5 metres (674 feet).

Subsequently, her sister ships, the *Royal Viking Sky* and *Royal Viking Sea*, were given the same treatment. They were not the first vessels to be 'jumbo-ised' in this fashion, though. A string of other cruise ships and ferries had earlier been modified likewise and there have been many more since. The practice has also been extended to other categories of merchant ships, notably the giant oil tanker *Seawise Giant*, the largest merchant vessel in the world. In 1981, she was stretched by 81 metres (266 feet) to give her the phenomenal tonnage measurements of 238,558 gross and 568,379 deadweight, and overall dimensions, in the enlarged state of 458 metres (1,504 feet) length and 69 metres (226 feet) beam, that enabled her to claim this record.

This practice of stretching or 'jumbo-ising' ships is not a recent development, owing itself principally to a quite amazing salvage operation undertaken in March 1907 to save the White Star liner *Suevic* which had been wrecked on the Stag Rock, near the Lizard Point, Cornwall, on the return leg of a voyage to Australia.

In an operation that earned her the reputation of being "the ship that would not die", a new bow section was added to her original stern and midships section permitting her to continue in active service for another 34 valuable years. Although she could not claim to be the first vessel to be so reconstructed, what made the *Suevic*'s re-generation such a spectacular feat was the complexity of the undertaking given the extent of contemporary technology and the fact that the critical phase of the operation was not performed in the sheltered surroundings of a drydock but at the scene of the accident, while the ship continued to pivot on the rocks upon which she had impaled herself.

Cutting the ship in two was achieved by the strategic placement of

(top) The Royal Viking Star *at the AG 'Weser' shipyard, Bremerhaven, cut in two in readiness for jumbo-ising.* AG 'Weser' Seebeckwerft

(above) The rebuilt, lengthened Royal Viking Star *undergoing sea trials after the completion of the jumbo-ising operation.* AG 'Weser' Seebeckwerft

numerous small charges of dynamite because oxy-acetylene cutting equipment had not then been developed. By these controlled explosions a relatively tidy separation was accomplished, vital for the following stages to be executed with accuracy if the reconstruction of the vessel was to remain financially viable.

The *Suevic* had been approaching the British Isles in a blinding snowstorm during that fateful night of 17 March when she crashed into the Stag Rock. It appears that, in the poor visibility, worsened by darkness and swirling sleet and spray, the ship's officers misjudged the distance and bearing to the Lizard lighthouse. Failure to use the leaded line in these circumstances, to determine the depth of the water, resulted in the accident. The Cadgwith and Coverack lifeboats went to the *Suevic's* aid, taking ashore, fortunately without mishap, all 382 persons that were on board.

The following day, attempts were made to refloat the *Suevic* by reversing her engines but even with the removal of all the undamaged cargo this proved impossible. The ship was held fast by the bow which was seriously damaged and leaking like a sieve. The stern end with the engine plant, by contrast, was not only unaffected but was, in fact, floating free and in excellent condition. However, the *Suevic* was exposed to gale force winds and the swell of Atlantic waves driven on to the Cornish coast.

It was evident that, unless she was removed soon, the entire ship was at risk of total loss. Many experienced salvage men believed that the best course of action was to abandon the *Suevic* to her fate even then, the traditional course of action in such situations, in order to save further, unnecessary cost. This was not the view of the Liverpool & Glasgow Salvage Association. Acting on behalf of the ship's owners, the White Star Line, they recommended instead the extremely bold action of detonating the ship just aft of the mortally damaged bow section in a bid to save the stern end.

There was little precedent for such a salvage attempt. A short while previously the Elder Dempster steamship *Milwaukee* had been recovered in a similar fashion, but whereas her reconstruction had been technically successful it had been achieved only at an unacceptably high cost. Similarly, the *Highland Fling* had been surgically rebuilt after stranding but hers too had been an unprofitable undertaking.

In spite of the fact that the operation surgically to reconstruct the *Suevic* was the biggest and most ambitious to date, ahead of contemporary technology and complicated by problems of her precarious and remote situation, the Salvage Association believed that it was financially viable and worthwhile to undertake. The underwriters were only interested in the cargo and had no concern with the recovery of the ship, for the hull insurance was borne by the *Suevic's* owners. Replacement costs were therefore the responsibility of the White Star

Line and, even at 1907 prices, a not inconsiderable sum would have been involved to build a new ship. As far as the crippled ship was concerned, for some 122 metres (400 feet) of her length she was sound and, significantly, it was this part of the ship that contained the engine room, boilers and passenger accommodation, all of which were undamaged. Salvage was, thus, a very worthwhile option to explore, for, if successful, it could save the White Star Line a considerable amount of money.

By this time, 20 March 1907, the *Suevic* had been virtually stripped of all cargo worth saving. This had been loaded aboard the salvage vessels *Ranger, Plover* and *Linnet*, from Liverpool, as well as numerous local barges and coasters that had been mustered at the scene. Having been adequately lightened, all was ready for the critical stage of the operation to commence.

Under the water, the lower part of the bows was a tangled mess of steelwork at the point where the swell had ground it on to the rocky pinnacle. The cargo holds in the forward part of the ship were also open to the sea with considerable damage to the hull plating. It was important to select the most suitable point at which the hull should be severed so that weak areas of the structure that might complicate the rebuilding phase might be avoided and yet to retrieve as much of the ship that was intact as possible. It was finally decided that the *Suevic* should be cut in two immediately abaft the island bridge.

Contemporary accounts suggest that the separation of the two halves of the *Suevic* was completed at a single stroke, by the simultaneous detonation of all the explosive charges positioned around the hull. In fact, the operation took several days and had to be undertaken in stages - first the keel bar, then the port side bottom, starboard side bottom, bilge to keel port side, bilge to keel starboard side, and so on. Finally, the separation was completed with the cutting of the side plating from the bilge keels to the water line.

The work was drawn out, by necessity, because the divers were only permitted to work on the sea bottom at high and low water when there was little or no tidal movement. Successful completion of each stage required very careful calculations to determine the size and precise placement of each charge. In the event the operation went off without a hitch and following the last detonations, at 08.36 on 2 April 1907, the *Suevic* successfully divided. A final lift of the buoyant stern, by the swell, assisted in parting it from the bow, permitting it to float free on an even keel.

Once afloat, the tugs *Blazer, Herculaneum* and *Ranger* swiftly secured the *Suevic's* after section in order to prevent it from running aground again on other rocks in the reef. The damaged bow section was abandoned where it lay and was eventually broken up by the pounding of the waves during the night of 9/10 May.

Amazingly, the half ship then made its way to Southampton largely

103

104

(top): The White Star liner Suevic *shortly after stranding on the Stag Rock on 17 March 1907.* Gibsons

(above): Assisted by the tugs Blazer, Ranger *and* Herculaneum, *the newly separated stern end of the Suevic pulls clear of the still-captive bow.* Gibsons

under its own steam, employing its still perfectly sound engine plant. The accompanying tugs provided assistance with steering but played no major part in towing the vessel to her destination. One can imagine the strange sight as the cluster of ships proceeded along the coast, the small tugs surrounding the much larger form of the truncated *Suevic* steaming stern first to minimise strain on the exposed bulkhead.

This was a matter of some importance and later, it was necessary to treat the new bow section the same when it was launched at Harland & Wolff, Belfast. It was sent down the slipway bow first to prevent the closing bulkhead, which was not intended to withstand great pressures, from being subjected to excessive strain.

During the voyage along the coast the quartet of vessels encountered some quite severe weather which led to the *Ranger* running aground. Two additional tugs were sent from Southampton to render assistance.

The *Suevic's* stern end finally arrived at the Test Quay at 09.30 on 4 April 1907, making her the first White Star liner ever to enter the port, a far from auspicious commencement to the long association between Southampton and the White Star company that was to follow.

Two days later, the *Suevic's* after end was drydocked for preliminary repairs in the Trafalgar drydock, owned and operated by Harland & Wolff. Work commenced with tidying up the plating, the damaged pipework and other fixtures and fittings that ran across the expanse of the exposed end to which a new bow section was to interface. The damaged side plating was removed for some distance aft of the exposed end, temporarily revealing the ship's metal framework, before replacement steel sheets were fitted. Simultaneously, the decking was shored up with heavy timbers to prevent collapse or distortion prior to the re-assembly with the new bow section. Men from the nearby Thornycroft shipyard at Woolston were hired to assist with the extensive repair work as it was hoped to get the *Suevic* back in service as soon as possible.

Soon after the successful partitioning of the wrecked ship had been accomplished, a new bow section was ordered from Harland & Wolff's shipyard at Queen's Island, Belfast, where the *Suevic* herself had been built originally. Constructed to the ship's original plans, it measured 64.6 metres (212 feet) in length, marginally longer than the severed bow, so that it would slightly overlap the salvaged stern end just beyond the after bulkhead of number 3 hold.

On a light note, it was claimed during this period that the *Suevic* was the longest passenger ship in the world, extending from her stern, in Southampton, to her bow, in Belfast!

Following its launch, on 5 October 1907, the bow section was completely fitted out in all respects in readiness for sea, including all masts and rigging, with lifeboats in davits on either side and the bridge structure fully equipped with navigational equipment, wheel and engine

105

106

(top): The Suevic's *stern end arrives at Southampton, revealing more clearly the condition of the ship at the fracture.* unknown source

(above): The ship's stern in the Trafalgar Dock at Southampton awaiting the arrival of the new bows. The decks are shored up with timbers. Nautical Photo Agency.

room telegraphs. Prior to departure for Southampton it was ballasted with a quantity of heavy machinery destined for the Harland & Wolff repair shops in the port, much of which was still in use up to recent times when Vosper Ship Repairers operated the Trafalgar Dock complex. A number of heavy pumps were also installed in case of leaks.

The new bow left Belfast under tow on 19 October 1907, travelling via the Irish Sea and around the Cornish coast, past the place where its abandoned predecessor had finally succumbed to the elements. The twin-funnelled paddle tug *Pathfinder* led the way, pulling the bow section bulkhead first, a perhaps surprising arrangement considering the risks to the bulkhead's integrity given its inability to withstand extreme force. The tug *Blazer*, secured astern, controlled the steering of the dumb bow structure.

Six days later, at 10.45 on 25 October 1907, after a temporary stop at Carrickfergus, because of bad weather experienced off the Tuskar Rock, the bow arrived at Southampton. First secured alongside the docks, it was later manoeuvred into the Trafalgar drydock to join the waiting midships and stern section which was, by then, ready for the re-assembly process. The tugs nudged the bow part as close as they could to the stern end, without risking collision and damage, a very delicate operation in the confined space of even this quite large dock, especially as it was conducted without the benefit of radio communications between those involved, as would be the practice today. Final adjustments, to draw the two sections together, were achieved using hydraulic rams erected in the dock bottom.

The workmen then set about joining the ship together again, riveting the overlapping plates, connecting together the metal framework, decks and deckheads, installing new bulkheads and linking up all the cables and pipework that extended from one end of the ship to the other through the fracture joint. This was no mean feat, both in terms of the extent of the work and its technical complexity, but everything was completed within three months, a great testimony to the effort and skill of these craftsmen.

The *Suevic* left drydock early in the new year, fully restored in readiness to resume her commercial service. Her first sailing was scheduled for 14 January 1908.

The reconstruction had been achieved in a remarkably short period of time, which was highly commendable, but what about the quality and durability of the surgery? By any standards the *Suevic*'s subsequent career from this point was of unusually long duration and of quite a strenuous character, serving to demonstrate that in her salvaged and rebuilt form she was as good as new. Following six more years on the Australia run out of Southampton, she spent almost five arduous and unbroken years on war work. She returned to the Australia service in 1920, continuing on it for another eight years and outliving two of her

107

sisters, and when, finally, she was sold in 1928 it was for further active duties. Like three others of her class, she was converted into a whaling mother ship for operations in the Atlantic under the Norwegian flag.

Her new owners had her converted at Kiel, renaming her *Skytteren*. The new tasks for which she was acquired continued up to just after the outbreak of World War 2 when she was interned at Gothenburg. On 1 April 1942, while attempting to escape to Great Britain, the *Skytteren* was intercepted off Maseskjaer, Sweden, by German naval vessels. To avoid capture, her crew was forced to scuttle her. She was then 42 years old, yet, in other circumstances, she might have remained in service for a good many more years. Significantly, some thirty four years of her life had been spent in her reconstructed state, a vindication of the judgement of both the Liverpool & Glasgow Salvage Association and her original owners, in embarking upon such a radical salvage, and a clear proof of the technical viability and financial justification of ship surgery. At the time, the rebuilding of the *Suevic* was pertinently described as "a doubtful experiment crowned with success of exceptional magnitude". How true this was!

Yet what could not have been appreciated then was the legacy that the *Suevic's* salvage left for the future. The benefits of improved performance, through greater capacity and earning power, enjoyed by today's jumbo-ised merchantmen are a constant reminder of this outstanding feat of pioneering salvage carried out 82 years ago.

108

(above): Rebuilt! The Suevic *after returning to service. Even close up it was almost impossible to distinguish her from her pre-accident appearance.* World Ship Photo Library

Oil on Troubled Waters

Until 1989, the practice of salvage at sea was conducted almost exclusively according to the principle of "No Cure - No Pay", established almost a hundred years earlier but formally introduced by the Brussels Convention of 1910.

The need to change the law governing salvage had become increasingly imperative as more and larger cargoes of toxic, radioactive and petro-chemical materials are shipped by sea. A series of major accidents involving oil tankers, beginning with the *Torrey Canyon* in March 1967 and extending up to the *Exxon Valdez* spill in January 1989, highlighted the pollution hazard that these cargoes pose. As yet there has not been an incident on a like scale in which vast quantities of toxic chemicals or radio-active waste have been spilt into the sea but the environmental damage that would be wreaked by such a catastrophe does not bear thinking about.

109

Through the work of the International Maritime Organisation (IMO) much effort has been made to minimise the possibility of such disasters - by improving the construction techniques and sea-keeping qualities of new vessels, by raising standards of navigation and seamanship, by introducing new regulations for traffic control and by encouraging the adoption of new technology designed to assist safer, accident-free navigation. But, despite all these very welcome initiatives, accidents still occur, if for no other reason than through the human factor, the one factor that cannot be easily regulated or legislated against.

Thus it has been from time to time, that prevention has failed and a swift and effective cure has become of paramount concern. In reality, this has meant calling upon the service of the salvage companies to provide timely intervention to contain the situation, followed by the removal of the source of pollution as soon as possible thereafter. In this day and age, increasingly pre-occupied with ecological mismanagement and environmental damage on a global scale, there have been growing demands for the shipping industry to get its house in order. Under the green spotlight nothing stands out more graphically as violations of this new found concern about the environment than front page headlines about miles of shoreline caked with black, foul-smelling crude oil, accompanied with photographs of dead and dying sea birds.

The problem was that, under the old type of salvage agreement, there was no incentive for salvage companies to take containment

measures to control pollution. "No Cure - No Pay" literally meant just that, so that deriving appropriate remuneration for their intervention depended on their ability successfully to recover the afflicted vessel as stipulated. In circumstances where such an objective appeared to be unachievable, salvage companies were naturally reluctant to commit costs in pursuit of a lost cause with little prospect of a reward.

The single incident that perhaps brought the situation to a head was the stranding of the *Amoco Cadiz* on the Brittany coast of north France in March 1978, depositing 230,000 tons of crude oil into the shallow coastal waters, severely polluting the shoreline from Trebeurden in the north to the Point de St. Mathieu in the west. Sadly, even this incredible extent of environmental damage paled into insignificance when compared with the *Exxon Vadez* incident but at the time it stimulated a far-reaching examination of the existing salvage arrangements, with a view to preventing a repetition of such a disaster.

In particular, the fact that a salvor might decline to offer his services at a time of emergency, if the prospect of earning a salvage award appeared too remote, was causing considerable concern. There were no legal provisions by which an authority or government could compel a salvage company's participation in such circumstances. It seemed that the time honoured principle of "No Cure - No Pay" was outdated.

At the request of the International Maritime Committee the National Marine Law Association set about studying the problem in all its aspects, including whether, in general terms, the financial rewards payable to salvors had failed to keep pace with the high cost of renewing and maintaining sophisticated salvage equipment.

In 1981 a new International Convention on Salvage was recommended which would introduce the quite new concept of joint responsibility, by salvors and ship owners, for preventing damage to the environment whenever a salvage operation is undertaken, with the payment of salvage rewards being made for either the preservation of property or the avoidance of environmental damage or both. These proposals were submitted to the International Maritime Organisation's Legal Committee in 1982 to permit interested states to consider and comment on them. This led to the production of a draft convention followed by a conference in April 1989, attended by 66 countries, at which the definitive wording of the new International Convention was finally decided. By the end of the conference the new Convention had been adopted.

As with other international legislation introduced through the IMO, the new Convention will enter into force one year after 15 member states have consented to be bound by it. In preparation for this, Lloyds' have introduced a new Open Form for future salvage agreements. This addresses the special provisions of Article 14, the section which covers

the compensation for salvors who take measures to prevent environmental damage.

At this time it is too early to make observations on the impact of the new Salvage Convention at work, in particular in so far as incidents involving oil tankers will benefit from its provisions. As the main purpose of this chapter is to focus on the salvage issues when dealing with tanker accidents, it is necessary to look back at events that occurred before the 1989 Convention. Irrespective of the payment arrangements that apply, the salvage techniques involved, peculiar to these types of situation, remain much the same. The point to make is, perhaps, that in the accounts that follow, the salvage companies concerned embarked upon the respective operations under the traditional "No Cure - No Pay" contractual terms with reasonable certainty of a positive outcome. Indeed, in each case, this was the final result.

During the evening of 23 October 1970, the 43,000 GRT Liberian registered motor tanker *Pacific Glory* was passing south of the Isle of Wight, bound from Bonny, Nigeria to Rotterdam with almost full tanks containing 70,000 tons of crude oil. Heading in the same general direction was the steam tanker *Allegro*, also flying the Liberian flag, out of Marsa el Brega, Saudi Arabia, destined for the Esso Fawley Refinery in Southampton Water. As the vessels crossed they came into collision, the accident resulting to some extent from confusion over right of way between two vessels having the same general bearing on gradually converging courses but also because, it was claimed, the *Allegro* was herself in the process of taking evasive action to avoid collision with yet a third, eastward-bound ship. The rules for such manoeuvres are quite clear but, as in the case of many similar incidents, the failure to adhere to the recognised procedures in a situation where the relative positions of the vessels concerned was in doubt, resulted in calamity.

Following the collision, fire erupted aboard the *Pacific Glory* and very soon most of the ship, aft of the main cargo tanks, was ablaze. The ship had considerable damage on her starboard side about a quarter of her length along from the stern. One of her starboard side storage tanks was fractured and significant amounts of oil were leaking into the sea through the hole though this was mainly burning off in the water. Initially, it was believed that the *Pacific Glory* had been holed by the *Allegro* in the collision but it was subsequently established that the impact had caused an explosion, the force of which had opened up the ship's side. Immediately following the collision, the pilot aboard the *Pacific Glory* had recommended to the ship's master that her engines should be stopped. He had rightly suspected that fuel lines to the engine had been ruptured and that the leaking fuel might ignite. Unfortunately, his swift thinking was not rewarded in kind for the explosion occurred before fuel supplies could be isolated and the engine room spaces ventilated.

The accident occurred approximately 11 kilometres (6 miles) to the

111

south of St Catherine's Point. Assistance, in the form of tugs and rescue craft, soon arrived on the scene. Even a cross-Solent hovercraft went to the stricken vessel's aid proving to be an ideal fast ferry for getting injured seamen ashore for hospital treatment in double quick time. By the following morning the *Pacific Glory* was surrounded by small craft, mainly Navy tugs from Portsmouth and harbour tugs from the Port of Southampton. No less than six were constantly spraying detergent to disperse oil while a further three were fighting the fire aboard the tanker with their high pressure hoses. Yet more were occupied in attempting to tow the drifting vessel to a more sheltered area where the fire could be more easily fought. This magnificent response was achieved as an extension to the "Operation Solfire" emergency plan, co-ordinated by the twin port authorities in the Solent area. Additionally, the frigate HMS *Zulu* was sent to the casualty scene to provide backup to the immediate rescue and salvage effort and to search for both survivors and the bodies of victims. Thirteen men lost their lives in the crash.

Meanwhile, the *Allegro*, which had not been so badly affected, had proceeded to Fawley to discharge and undergo a detailed survey prior to continuing her voyage to Rotterdam.

The tugs towing the *Pacific Glory* were not, in the event, able to move her far. The ship was rapidly settling, heavily down by the stern and awash along her starboard side. She finally came to rest in shallow water about 10 kilometres (5 miles) from the Nab Tower with the wind backing on to her, threatening to spread the fire along her length, towards her bow.

The authorities were confronted with a dangerous and rapidly deteriorating situation with a number of potentially unwelcome outcomes, each necessitating different remedial actions. The *Pacific Glory* was engulfed by a fiercely blazing, out-of-control fire. This was spreading in the direction of unaffected cargo in the fore-part of the ship and, if ignited, there was a possibility that this would detonate. Oil was leaking in increasing quantities within close proximity of some of southern England's most famous holiday beaches and a stiff south westerly breeze seemed certain to ensure that the spillage would reach shore. There was also a risk that the *Pacific Glory* would sink altogether, interfering with the freedom of navigation of other shipping heading for the Solent past the Nab Tower.

At this time, the Royal Navy had assumed responsibility for co-ordinating the response, concentrating all the immediate effort on tackling the fire. In the late evening of 24 October the fire was being contained at a point about 3 metres (10 feet) forward of the aftercastle but beyond the next bulkhead were some 10,000 tons of oil. Due to the damage to the ship none of the on board fire-fighting facilities could be utilised. In order to limit its spread the Navy endeavoured to have the ship's head turned into the wind.

That night, on the high tide, a bid was made to rotate the stricken tanker using six of the tugs that were on station but it proved impossible to move her at all. The next opportunity would be at the time of the next high tide the following day but, on the insistence of a fire officer aboard one of the tugs, this effort to turn the *Pacific Glory* bow into the wind was abandoned before it could recommence. He was concerned that any perceived advantage of turning her was more than outweighed by the risk that the stern might break off during the process.

Slicks of spilt oil were evident in the sea by this time, one extending over 5.5 kilometres (3 miles) long at a distance of about 2.75 kilometres (1 miles) from the casualty on her starboard side. Reports were also starting to come in from places along the south coast, indicating that oil pollution in small amounts had affected the shoreline from Hove to Hastings and even as far afield as Rye and Dungeness. The weather was also deteriorating as autumn gales set in, aggravating the situation further.

During the night of 25/26 October a particularly severe gale blew up causing the ship to pound heavily on the bottom. Fears that she might break up were rather over pessimistic but two tugs were required to hold the tanker's bow securely until the storm had blown itself out. The frigate HMS *Andromeda*, which had relieved HMS *Zulu*, also stood by. By the morning the vessel had settled even more at the stern but there was no sign of any weakening of the ship's structural integrity. She was stranded in sand and shingle with her stern end now buried some 5.5 metres (18 feet). Her poop was about 2.5 metres (8 feet) below sea level at half tide. Shell International, the charterers of the tanker, announced that L. Smit & Company Internationale Sleepdienst (Smit Tak) had been called in to assist with the refloating and removal of the *Pacific Glory*.

By now, in spite of the problems caused by the weather, the fire had been brought under control so that the vessel could be boarded. At 18.00 hours on 26 October it was considered to have been extinguished completely, permitting a preliminary inspection to take place. This revealed that the entire superstructure of the tanker had been gutted and destroyed and that her engine room and pump room were flooded. Her main deck was severely buckled and many centre deck strakes in the vicinity of her pump room were fractured. If it was possible to refloat her successfully, it was still going to cost a great deal of money to restore her for further service.

Having effectively contained the situation, the next stage of the plan of action was to lighten the *Pacific Glory* sufficiently to permit her removal to a deeper water site where further cargo removal and other preparatory actions could be taken prior to transferring her to a drydock for repairs. For this, the Shell-owned steam tanker *Halia* was employed, arriving in the area at 07.50 on 27 October when she anchored off Spithead, 1.85 kilometres (1 mile) south of Fort Gilkicker Point.

Two days later, the *Halia* berthed alongside the *Pacific Glory* and

113

*(right): Down
at the stern
and belching
smoke from
the fire
raging within
her, the*
Pacific Glory
Portsmouth
Publishing &
Printing

(right): The
Pacific Glory
and Halia
*alongside
each other
during the
lightening
process.*
Associated
Press

the off-loading of the cargo of Nigerian crude oil commenced. The two vessels were secured together port side to port side. The first of the *Pacific Glory's* five tanks to be emptied was No 4 tank, the last but one to the stern. Of six available pumps only four could be used owing to the inaccessibility of sufficient Butterworth openings. However, the four pumps that were operational commenced work at 18.20 on 29 October and, after fifteen hours' pumping, some 1,130 tons of cargo had been transferred. With an estimated 60,000 tons of oil remaining aboard the *Pacific Glory*, the salvors did not regard this performance as acceptable and earnestly sought methods by which the pumping rate could be improved. At Fawley refinery, meanwhile, a holding tank was swiftly commissioned which would enable the *Halia* rapidly to discharge the off-loaded oil to permit a fast turn round and return to the casualty. Over a period of some hours the pumping rate was gradually increased to 160 tons per hour but a further break-up of the weather in the afternoon of 30 October compelled the salvage team to suspend the operation. It had become too rough for the *Halia* to remain alongside the *Pacific Glory* so the ships were separated and the *Halia* shifted to a nearby anchorage, 1.85 kilometres (1 mile) to the west, to await an improvement in the weather conditions.

Almost six days were lost due to the interruption, continuing bad weather delaying the resumption of the off-loading operation until 19.15 on 5 November. Divers were finally able to carry out an underwater inspection at this time. This showed that the *Pacific Glory* had a large hole in the shell of number five tank on her starboard side, estimated to be 10 metres (33 feet) deep and extending aft to the engine room where it narrowed to a depth of 7 metres (23 feet).

Progress in lightening the tanker soon picked up again. Although she was still drawing 18.25 metres (60 feet) of water at her aft end, on 6 November the port auxiliary vessel *Prompt* was sent to the scene from Portsmouth Dockyard to provide steam to the *Pacific Glory's* windlass in order to weigh her anchor. It was anticipated that she would refloat on the 17.00 high tide that day, when salvors would tow her to a new position 7.5 to 9.25 kilometres (4 to 5 miles) to the southeast of her existing position. There, the transfer of cargo would continue while her forepeak was ballasted to restore her trim.

Having refloated her and with lightening by the *Halia* continuing, the salvors next proposed to move the *Pacific Glory* to the sheltered waters of the Solent to complete their work. This was prevented, however, by the issuing of a High Court injunction which instructed them instead to transfer her to a position off the Devon/Dorset coast, in Lyme Bay.

At 23.35 on 6 November, the *Halia* cast off for the last time having removed 6,224 tons of oil. Once more the *Prompt* provided steam to raise the *Pacific Glory's* anchor and then she was towed by the tug

Noordzee, in the direction of Lyme Bay, accompanied by numerous other vessels. In the worsening weather, one of these, the small tug *Harry Sharman,* ran aground in Sandown Bay depositing a large quantity of detergent into the sea precipitating another, quite different, pollution problem.

In the event, the *Pacific Glory* re-anchored in Torbay, 4 kilometres (2 miles) east of Hope's Nose. The salvors' ultimate intentions were to take the *Pacific Glory* to Rotterdam but the authorities there requested that, as she would be under tow when entering the port, her draught should not exceed 15.25 metres (50 feet). Normally, a vessel manoeuvring into the port under her own power was permitted to draw a maximum of 19.25 metres (63 feet).

On 11 November, the salvage team declared that the tanker was virtually ready for the move. Her hull had been temporarily patched and, after all night pumping, the stern draught had been reduced to 16 metres (53 feet). Further work, to return her to an even keel, would ensure that her overall, extreme draught was within the required limits.

At 14.36 on 13 November, under tow of the *Noordzee,* the *Pacific Glory* headed east, around Portland Bill, proceeding to the Strait of Dover and then the Netherlands. The convoy reached the entrance of the Nieuwe Waterweg in the afternoon of 17 November where the *Noordzee* was relieved by four harbour tugs. They in turn delivered the *Pacific Glory* to the Europort Buoy number 1 where the Lloyds Open Form contract was formally terminated.

At a time, many years before the introduction of the special pollution prevention rules of the new International Salvage Convention, a serious disaster had been averted and environmental damage significantly minimised by the timely intervention of salvage experts.

Such a positive outcome had depended, though, on the confidence of the salvage team in its ability to save the ship.

The *Pacific Glory* herself lingered at Rotterdam for many months. After transferring to Europoort's Petroleumhaven, where the remainder of her cargo was discharged, she was moved to the tanker cleaning installation at Schiedam on 24 December 1970. Nearly a month later, on 21 January 1971, she was drydocked at the Wilton-Fijenoord shipyard for inspection and for basic repairs to render her seaworthy. Though undocked on 1 February it was not until 13 December, that same year, that the *Pacific Glory* finally left Rotterdam under tow of the tugs *Roode Zee* and *Witte Zee,* bound for Hong Kong. Arriving there on 6 March 1972, she was taken in hand for complete reconstruction including the building of a totally new after end. She finally re-emerged on 11 November 1972 under the new name *Oriental Confidence.*

Another, quite different, salvage operation involving an oil tanker required the salvors to deal with wreck removal for scrap rather than recovery for reconstruction. Again, Smit Tak was the company engaged

to undertake the work. This salvage story relates to an accident on 8 January 1979, on which date a quite horrific explosion ripped through the French registered *Betelgeuse* while she was discharging cargo at the Whiddy Island oil terminal at Bantry Bay, Ireland. Apparently triggered by her hull cracking, as indicated by subsequent metallurgic tests, the explosions, which occurred simultaneously in number 4 and number 6 tanks, wreaked incredible devastation, breaking the vessel into three distinct sections. Immediately following the explosion, there was a frightening conflagration as lighted oil on the surface burnt off, the flames visible for a distance of 300 kilometres (160 miles) and preventing fire-fighters and rescue services from approaching nearer than 185 metres (600 feet) from the partly submerged wreck. Over the scene, a vast pall of black oily smoke billowed upwards hanging in the air for days afterwards.

The loss of life too was terrible, affecting the entire crew of the tanker as well as local inhabitants working ashore at the Gulf oil terminal, 51 persons in total being killed in the explosion. The members of seven families whose homes were on Whiddy Island fled for their lives in rowing boats.

The jetty, alongside which the *Betelgeuse* had been secured, was completely wrecked and the immediate concern was that the fire would spread deeper into the terminal complex, to the main storage tanks. Fire gangs from Bantry, Skibbereen and Dunmanway were rushed to the scene to assist the Gulf Oil fire crews based at the terminal.

The immediate problems posed by the disaster were recovering bodies and providing comfort for the bereaved and shocked community, and containing the spillage of oil which threatened serious pollution. The fact that the fire was raging and the wreck inaccessible was frustrating all efforts to deal with the latter problem in anything but a cosmetic fashion. Bantry Bay, in which Whiddy Island is located, is designated an area of outstanding natural beauty (making it, perhaps, a rather strange choice as the place to construct an oil terminal). But apart from the concern about oil pollution spoiling the nearby shoreline, it was feared that the local fishing industry would also suffer as a consequence of oil deposits settling on herring spawning grounds and scallop beds.

The sunken tanker looked like putting a section of the terminal out of action for a long time, reducing its operational capability by a significant margin which in turn could affect the livelihoods of other local citizens. Within two weeks of the disaster, three VLCCs (very large crude carriers) and three shuttle tankers had to be re-directed. Repairs to the oil terminal were forecast to cost at least £15 million.

The explosions had left the mid and aft sections of the 61,766 GRT *Betelgeuse*, submerged in 30 metres (100 feet) or more of water, lying on the sea-bed beneath the berth. The bow section, which was still partly connected to the midships section by the deck plating, was still floating but, restrained as it was, only the bow itself protruded above the water,

118

(above): The Betelgeuse *after the explosion, on fire and totally wrecked.*
Lloyds List

(below): Diagramatic representation of the disposition of the Betelgeuse's
three sections following the explosion. Birkenhead Associates

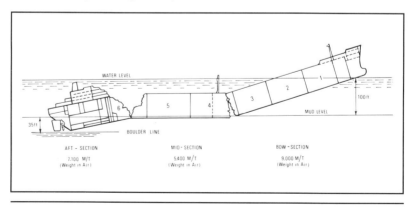

pointing skywards.

It was evident that there was little prospect of salving the *Betelgeuse* for anything but breaking up so that the ensuing operation, by necessity, became one of wreck removal. Again, Smit Tak engaged to carry out this work and advance parties of the company's surveyors and salvage strategists promptly arrived on the scene on 9 January to assess the situation. By the following day a contract to clear the three sections of the wrecked tanker had been successfully negotiated. The agreement, made with the West of England P & I Club (The West of England Ship Owners Mutual Protection and Indemnity Association), of which the ship's owners were a member, was on a continual assessment basis. With so many unknown factors, Smit Tak had been compelled to decline from agreeing a contract on a fixed price basis. The salvage operation involved the lifting and removal from a very restricted position of each of the parts of the wreck as a complete piece. The bow section alone, the heaviest of the three, was estimated to weigh over 9,000 tons. Raising, and floating clear, structures of this size, in these circumstances would be no mean feat.

Before the contract had been concluded with Smit Tak, the fire had been extinguished. Divers were therefore able to survey the wreck underwater to determine better how it was situated. About 45,000 tons of cargo was still estimated to be remaining in the midships section but this was leaking from the ship at the rate of five tons per hour. Already some 3.75 kilometres (2 miles) of nearby coastline had been affected and detergent spraying was proceeding in earnest. This in itself created something of a dilemma for it was feared that the chemical dispersants being used would cause more damage to marine life than the leaking oil. After due consideration of the balance of the risk, detergent spraying was suspended.

Vital elements of Smit Tak's specialised salvage equipment had been mobilised immediately the company had been engaged for the operation and they now began to arrive on the scene. The supply vessel *Smit Lloyd 107* and the salvage vessel *Barracuda* arrived in Bantry Bay on 13 and 14 January respectively. Later, the heavy lift barge *Taklift 1*, with its massive sheerlegs, and the pontoon barge *Giant 1* would join them.

The Smit Tak plan of action was to remove the three parts of the wreck in sequence, commencing with the bow section and finishing with the stern section. First, the remnants of cargo in the forward tanks had to be pumped out, through floating hose, to one of the tanks on Whiddy Island. Though the pipes had a capacity of 4,000 tons an hour, the oil was discharged at a painfully slow rate, the best performance achieved being no more than 150 to 170 tons per hour. Between 19 and 25 January around 10,000 tons of oil were pumped ashore to the tank farm.

In order to remove the bow section it had first to be detached from the centre section but any form of cutting to achieve this was out of the

119

question. Resulting from the discharge of oil from the bow section, the tanks in the forward section now contained explosive gases. Before any work could proceed these areas had to be filled with inert gases, an operation that took two anxious days, during which time the risk of further explosions was ever present.

It had been hoped that the extra buoyancy of the section, achieved through lightening it, would have been sufficient alone to break it free from the midships section. In the event, because the connection was stronger than had been thought, it actually caused the midships section to lift off the bottom and this was now exploited to advantage. Lengths of heavy duty wire and chain cable were passed beneath this section of the wreck to act as slings, to be utilised at a later date, to assist in its lifting and removal.

As the two sections had not separated as expected, more drastic measures were called for. An attempt was made to drag the bow section away using the *Smit Lloyd 107* but this too failed. The salvage team was left no choice but to deliberately ballast and deballast the bow section until the connection was stressed to destruction.

Supported by compressed air, the bow section was then towed clear of the jetty to a protected anchorage where a team of experts inspected it on behalf of the committee of inquiry which was investigating the disaster. At last, on 22 February 1979, the bow section was towed out into the Atlantic by the *Smit Lloyd 107*, accompanied by the Irish corvette *Deirdre*. There it was sunk in a part of the ocean that was more than 2,000 metres (6,500 feet) deep, in position latitude, 50° 42'N, longitude 12° 04'W.

Attention was now turned to the midships section of the *Betelgeuse* which was found, beneath the water, to be still attached to the stern section. Removal of these final sections proved to be difficult and the initial good progress made by the salvage team was now lost as more and more obstacles were encountered. The disturbance of the midbody, by the manner of removal of the bow section, had left it, at its forward end, deeply buried in the mud so that even with the powerful lifting capacity of the *Taklift 1's* sheerlegs, it could not be budged.

A quite different approach had to be devised by the salvage team if clearance of the midships section was to be accomplished. They contrived to provide extra buoyancy in this section, first by patching the holes in it and then by pumping compressed air into the concealed compartments. Any compartments that could not be made fully airtight were injected with polystyrene pallets. The preparatory work to lift the midbody, estimated to weigh 5,400 tons, lasted over several months with a team of sixteen divers working round the clock in poor visibility and waters that were persistently affected by the swell coming in from the Atlantic. Finally, on 27 August 1979, with two tanks pressurised with 1,400 cubic metres of compressed air and a further two tanks filled with

6,000 cubic metres of polystyrene, the midships section lifted off the mud. But for the fact that it was still attached to the stern section it would undoubtedly have floated to the surface.

Detachment of the two sections was thus the next stage of the operation. This was achieved by dragging the *Betelgeuse's* anchor chain, one of the chains positioned under the midships section months earlier, under the hull to the point of the fracture, and then using it literally to saw through the remnants of structure that still connected the two parts together. This was performed by the *Taklift 1* but, as an indication of the strength of construction of the crippled tanker, in spite of the fact that structural weaknesses were suspected as having been the cause of the disaster, this took three days and three nights to complete, working continuously.

Once separated, the midbody section of the *Betelgeuse* was dragged away to a sheltered anchorage where it remained for the next three months. Here, the salvage team continued with its efforts to increase its buoyancy in order to float it on to the submersible barge *Giant 1*, for removal to the scrap yard. Floating the section sufficiently high to provide clearance over the barge proved hard to achieve. A lot of additional patching and pumping out was necessary and all of it according to precise calculations, for the trim and stability of the section were equally important. If too much buoyancy was created on one side, it could easily roll over or adopt an inclination that would make transferring it to the barge even more difficult.

On 9 December the requisite clearance was obtained and the operation to manoeuvre the section over the barge began. Even at this point fresh problems arose. As the section was clearing the edge of the barge, divers discovered a large piece of metal protruding underneath which had, until that point, been hidden from their view. The team had a clear choice: either to cut the offending obstacle away, which could introduce further delays or to swing the section round and attempt to position it on the barge athwartships, leaving the plating clear over the side so that it could be cut away there, whenever convenient. In pursuing the latter approach, there would be a measure of risk to the barge during the ensuing voyage to the scrapyard, if rough weather was encountered. Nevertheless the team opted for this approach, as the risk was calculated and could be ameliorated by further manoeuvring, if necessary. On 20 December, after much adjustment and realignment, the midships section was loaded on the barge and raised to the surface. Secured in place there, the *Giant 1* left Bantry Bay with it, under tow of the salvage tug Witte Zee, on 9 February. Four days later it arrived at Bilbao, Northern Spain, where it was broken up.

Only the after section remained to be cleared but in truth this presented the greatest challenge, yet already some fourteen months had passed since the disaster. A certain amount of preliminary work on the

121

122

(top): The salvaged centre section of the Betelgeuse *is towed away for scrapping after the successful completion of the second phase of the "3-in-1" salvage operation.* Lloyds List

(above): The stern section of the Betelgeuse *high and dry on the barge* Giant I *with the* Smit Salvage *team who were responsible for the successful recovery operation. The wreck reveals where the lift wires cut into the side of the hull.* Smit International

stern section had been under way during the latter stages of the effort to deal with the midships section. Now all effort was concentrated on clearing this final piece of wreckage which it was hoped to have removed before the end of that summer. The Gulf Oil Company was anxious to resume full operations at the oil terminal while the West of England P & I Club was becoming increasingly concerned at the mounting cost of the salvage operation.

Having pondered all the options available to them, the salvage crew determined that there was realistically only one viable approach open to them to successfully remove this 7,100 ton section which, by now, had settled 11 metres (36 feet) into the mud. This was to lift it bodily clear of the bottom in one piece and then raise it a further 36.5 metres (120 feet) to the surface, in order to float it clear, an operation of a magnitude for which there was no precedent in salvage history.

The lifting capacity required to heave a body of this mass would be at least 11,000 tons, totally overshadowing the 1,000 tons capacity immediately available from the *Taklift 1,* at the time the largest floating sheerlegs in the world.

It was decided that the additional lift capacity required could be obtained by modifying four flat-top pontoons, the *Giant 21, Giant 22, Jasmin Turtle* and *Daring Turtle.* The two *Giant* pontoons were equipped with two 1,500 ton hydraulic pulling units each while the other two barges were fitted with conventional winch gear. In total, the four pontoon barges would provide, in their modified state, more than the 11,000 tons lifting capacity required.

For the lifting operation, four cradle slings were constructed out of 28 lengths of 98mm diameter wire. In order to place these under the remaining part of the wreck, the mud around it had to be dredged away. This dredging work commenced on 15 March 1980 but hit difficulties almost immediately because the mud had a very firm consistency. The Smit engineers calculated that the mud was so firm that it was actually supporting the wreck and that it was probably safe, therefore, to tunnel through it, beneath the fore-part of the section. This would permit a quicker placement of the fore-end cradles than would be possible by persisting with dredging in a general fashion, as had been originally intended. A 40 metre (130 foot) tunnel was cut immediately beneath the ship's pump room permitting the forward slings, each 130 metres (425 feet) long, to be expeditiously positioned.

As the aft end of the stern section had settled deeper than the forward end, this tunnelling operation could not be repeated there. Instead, this end had to be pivoted upwards to bring it to a horizontal position so that the aft strops could be fitted into place. To do this, the *Giant 22* was positioned over the wreck and a series of wires paid out and passed through the propeller arch. A 'saddle' device was fitted over these wires, at the point where they passed through the propeller arch, so that

they would not be severed by its sharp edge profile when the 3,000 tons lift from the *Giant 22* was applied. The stern end was hoisted on 4 June 1980, requiring almost all the available lifting power of the *Giant 22* to free it from the suction of the bottom mud. There was great concern at one point that the aft section of the *Betelgeuse* might be cut in two as the wires bit deep into the metal structure but the 'saddle' performed its task and the wires held. With sufficient clearance obtained, divers were able to fix the aft end slings into place the very next day.

All that remained to be done now was for the four flat-top pontoons to exercise their lifting capabilities in synchronisation, to raise the stern section on an even keel. This was initially programmed for 23 June 1980 but unseasonably inclement weather forced a postponement until 1 July. With weight indicators displaying the weight of the wreck all through the critical operation, while other instruments showed its trim and attitude, the final section of the wreck was gingerly raised from the sea-bed until it was suspended just 2 metres (6.5 feet) below the surface. The exercise had broken new ground in salvage practice but, due to the careful pre-planning and co-ordination of the operation, it went as smoothly as if it had been repeatedly performed.

The danger of oil spillage still remained, even at this time, just as it had done when each of the previous sections of wreck had been disturbed. Therefore, prior to removal, the section was surrounded by oil booms placed in position by a team from Smit Tak's Anti-Pollution Services Division. Then, transferred to a quiet area beyond Whiddy Island, the final act of the drama was played out as the section was pumped dry in readiness for loading it on to a submersible barge. On 17 September 1980 the final remnants of the *Betelgeuse* left Bantry, towed away to Barcelona by the tug *Zwarte Zee* secured aboard the semi-submersible *Giant 1*.

In the company's customary, professional manner, Smit Tak had dealt with a difficult salvage problem, permitting full scale operations at the Gulf Oil terminal to resume while preventing the local environment from being more seriously spoilt either by a massive release of oil or through the arbitrary dumping of unsightly pieces of rusting wreckage.

Only one question remained to be asked - what had actually caused the *Betelgeuse* to explode in the first place? When the committee of enquiry's findings were published they were a serious indictment of the ship's owners and operators. They reported that the "hull was seriously weakened due to inadequate and improper maintenance and excessive stress caused by incorrect ballasting".

Needle in a Haystack

The 20th century has seen progress of an unrivalled magnitude, unlike any similar period in history since the first inhabitation of this planet by the human species.

It has witnessed the conquest of the air, quite literally from the flimsy experiments of Kitty Hawk to the supersonic reality of Concorde and the landing of the first men on the Moon. Before 1900 the only persons to venture aloft had embarked on balloons or lighter-than-air craft.

Throughout the same period, the development of the motor car has advanced at an accelerating pace from the horseless carriages of the Edwardian era to the 965 kilometres per hour (600 miles per hour) speeds of Thrust II and its challengers for the land speed record. And it has been much the same in the fields of communication and computing.

Back in the early part of the century, such achievements were regarded with awe by the public at large, almost as though they were feats of magic, but as the decades have passed the "wonders" of science and technology have been received increasingly, with a sort of nonchalance, as normal and commonplace. It has almost become routine expectation that similar quantum leaps of progress will be achieved in all areas of technology, and salvage is no exception to this.

It is certainly true that salvage technology has kept pace with other, contemporary developments to the extent that it has come a very long way in even the last half-century. The requirements of ever more demanding challenges have stimulated progress in the development of both new recovery equipment and techniques. Still, it comes as something of a surprise to realise that the limit of free diving only fifty years ago was just 45.75 metres (150 feet) and the deepest that a bathysphere craft had ventured was a mere 915 metres (3,027 feet).

Apart from extending the depths to which divers and recovery vehicles can safely go in the course of routine work, salvage technique has also been advanced significantly in respect of the ability to pinpoint and recover all manner of unusual objects from the deep ocean floor - objects that often present particular complications due to their smallness of size, delicateness, difficulty to locate or inaccessibility.

In this chapter, I am recounting three incidents involving the retrieval of aircraft or objects related to aircraft which, by virtue of their size and the vastness of the ocean in which they were lost, could be

125

126

*(top): The nuclear bomb that was recovered from the sea bed off Spain,
safely stowed aboard the United States Navy's salvage vessel USS* Petrel.
*Looking on are Sr. Don Antonio Velilla Manteca (Chief of the Spanish
Nuclear Energy Board), Brig-Gen Arturo Monzet Touzet (Coordinator,
Spanish SAR Operations), Rear-Ad William S. Guest (Commander of US
Navy Task Force 65) and Maj-Gen Delmar E. Wilson (Commander 16th
Air Force).* US National Archives

*(above): The CURV-1 submersible used in the salvage of the lost nuclear
bomb.* US National Archives

likened to "needles in a haystack" in the challenge they presented to the recovery teams concerned. In each case they were dealing with intricate or delicate objects which required special location and lift methods to be devised.

When, in 1966, the United States Air Force lost, of all things, a nuclear bomb in the sea off Palomares, Spain, it caused quite a stir. Apart from the acute embarrassment caused by such a mishap involving a major military power and the attendant security issues, alarm about radiation pollution destroying fish spawning grounds needed to be quelled.

The bomb was one of four and the fact that two of them had impacted on land, breaking open and scattering plutonium and uranium over the surrounding countryside only added to the concern over the future livelihood of local fishermen if the one in the sea had ruptured likewise, causing a major ecological disaster. Simply testing the water to demonstrate that radiation leaks had not occurred would clearly be totally inadequate in the circumstances. In order fully to reassure the inhabitants of Palomares, it was essential that the missing bomb was located and recovered, regardless of cost. Subsequently, it would also have to be displayed to demonstrate conclusively that it had indeed been found and was intact.

The scene was therefore set for what was to become the most expensive salvage operation ever conducted. A fleet of eighteen ships and 2,200 men took part in the operation which, by its completion, had cost the United States Navy $30 million (£12.5 million at then- contemporary exchange rates).

Palomares is a, small coastal village near Almeria, in the south east corner of Spain. It was unexpectedly thrust under the international spotlight on 17 January 1966 when problems encountered by a massive US Air Force B-52 Stratofortress bomber during a routine aerial refuelling operation, six miles to the south above the Mediterranean, caused it to go out of control and crash. As it plunged earthwards, its four 20-megaton hydrogen-bombs were jettisoned in a bid to minimise the risk of radiation pollution, the pilot expecting them all to fall relatively safely into the sea. Apart from the two that hit the ground and broke open and the one that did fall into the sea, the fourth was recovered intact after embedding itself in soft ground. There was no risk of a nuclear explosion because the weapons, each of which measured 3.05 metres (10 feet) in length and weighed 1,270 kilograms (2,800 pounds), had not been in a primed state when released.

The principal problem confronting the recovery team was how to locate the bomb. The sea-bed along the Almeria coast shelves steeply to a considerable depth with the bottom consistency being mainly soft mud. The bomb was almost certainly completely enshrouded in this ooze, making it even more difficult to pinpoint.

With little scope for homing in on the bomb by electronic means,

the search team elected to organise a visual search using the 13 ton midget research submersible *Alvin* which was flown in specially from Pasadena, California. It was believed that the bomb's parachute was still attached and that this would assist in visibly locating it.

When organising an underwater search of any kind, when there is little information to indicate the whereabouts of the hunted object, the overriding priority is to reduce the search area through the adoption of efficient scanning procedures. There are numerous techniques for searching underwater, by sight, touch and sonar, employing free or tethered divers and manned or robot submarines. The choice depends on the depth and clarity of the water, the size of the object being sought and the extent of any pre-sortie knowledge as to its approximate location.

In the case of the *Titanic*, the ship was known to lie in one of the deepest parts of the Atlantic, approximately 3.6 kilometres (2.25 miles) down but her final position prior to sinking, the place from which any search for her would have to start, was indefinite because she had continued moving ahead for some distance from the point of impact with the iceberg. Consequently, the search team gathered under the leadership of Dr Richard Ballard of the Woods Hole Oceanographic Institute of Martha's Vineyard, Massachusetts, was confronted with the prospect of searching, at extreme depth, a vast sea area. Constraints of cost and adverse weather meant that this would be impossible to achieve unless an efficient method of sonar scanning was adopted - one that would provide the maximum coverage with the absolute minimum of effort, but not one so sparse that there would be a risk of missing the wreck altogether.

The approach adopted by the group involved sweeping horizontally, at regular intervals, across the ship's projected path from the point of collision. Computer calculations of the ship's final movements were based on the best information available from all documented sources. Each sweep extended a considerable distance beyond this path on either side, progressively following its general direction. The method proved to be successful and the subsequent, spectacular revelation of the discovery of the *Titanic*, complete with detailed photographs, is now well documented.

Other deep ocean search techniques are derived from the same basic principles exploited by Dr. Ballard's team, being utilised for a range of subsea activities from mineral exploration to oceanographic research and salvage.

The *Titanic* search strategy was a typical two-dimensional scan in the horizontal plane. The same basic technique can also be employed for two-dimensional scans in the vertical plane. The types of search pattern used vary considerably. In any given plane they can be criss-cross or 'U' pattern, square spiral, circular spiral, alternating semi-circular along a straight line, circular in steps and so on. In all cases, the most efficient use of resources is the paramount consideration. With accurate plotting

of search co-ordinates, unnecessary duplication of effort can be completely eliminated.

By employing techniques such as those described, the lost H-bomb was eventually located on 17 March 1966 lying in 760 metres (2,500 feet) of water. The discovery itself was not without drama for it occurred rather more by chance than by design. While routinely checking an area of the sea-bed, in order to eliminate it from the search, the *Alvin* ran blindly into the bomb's parachute and became completely entangled in it. Any elation there might have been over the discovery of the bomb was swiftly suppressed by concerns over the craft's predicament. There ensued quite a struggle to get it free, though fortunately it was successful. In fact, those aboard the *Alvin* were lucky to escape with their lives for they were beyond the reach of divers and no other suitable submersibles were available to carry out a rescue.

Having extricated themselves, the position of the bomb was marked in readiness for the recovery phase of the operation to commence.

The first bid to raise the bomb was made on 21 March using the *Alvin* alone but this failed when the cable attached to the bomb snapped-causing it to fall further, finally settling on a mud bank 870 metres (2,850 feet) down. No further attempts were made using only the equipment to hand because of the danger of causing the bomb to slip even deeper. Instead, more specialised equipment was flown in from the United States including extra strong cable and a special electronic retrieving device. Known as a CURV or Cable-controlled Underwater Recovery Vehicle, this came from the US Navy's Undersea Warfare Engineering Station (Naval Ocean Systems Command) based at San Diego, California.

129

Operated from the submarine rescue ship USS *Petrel*, the CURV successfully hooked onto the H-bomb and brought it to the surface. On 8 April 1966, at precisely 7.45am, the deceptively innocuous-looking silver cylinder was finally lifted aboard the mother ship. It was heavily dented but, to the profound relief of all on board, otherwise undamaged.

Ten years on, in 1976, while participating in naval manoeuvres in adverse weather conditions, an expensive and highly sophisticated United States Navy F-14 Tomcat fighter aircraft was lost off the deck of the aircraft carrier USS *John F. Kennedy*. The accident occurred in the vicinity of Scapa Flow in the Orkney Islands, north of Scotland.

At the time this aircraft was one of America's most advanced combat planes and there was, naturally enough, great concern that it should be quickly recovered lest it should fall into unfriendly hands which would undoubtedly subject it to close scrutiny.

Unlike civil aircraft, the F-14 did not carry either a transponder device or an acoustic beacon emitting a signal which would enable it to be quickly located. All that US Navy salvors had to go by, to trace the missing aircraft, was the approximate geographical co-ordinates of the position where it had been lost. They also had at their disposal a side

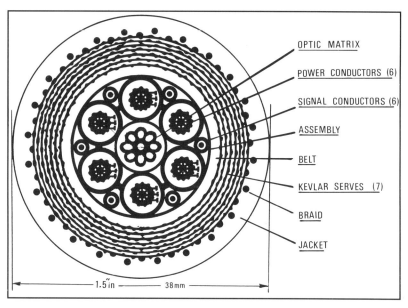

OPTIC MATRIX

POWER CONDUCTORS (6)

SIGNAL CONDUCTORS (6)

ASSEMBLY

BELT

KEVLAR SERVES (7)

BRAID

JACKET

1.5″in — 38mm

130

(top): Cross-section of the Kevlar umbilical control link used with the CURV vehicles. US Navy

(above): The CURV-III underwater recovery vehicle being handled aboard the oil rig supply ship Constructor *prior to being utilised to assist the recovery of the sunken F14A Tomcat fighter.* US National Archives

scan sonar system normally used to search for mines.

Working back and forth across sea areas positively targetted by this sonar, two salvage vessels trailed between them a heavy wire choker that extended to the sea floor, 610 metres (2,000 feet) down, with which they hoped to snag the lost fighter. This seemingly random approach in fact soon paid off. Once the salvage crews had hooked up to the aircraft, one end of the wire line, suitably looped, was passed down the other, with the assistance of divers, to provide a secure attachment to the plane's undercarriage.

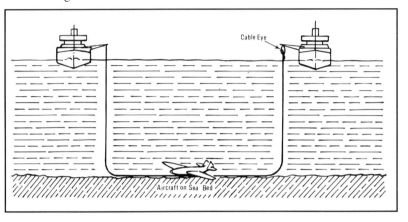

131

(above):The technique used to dredge for the sunken fighter aircraft. Once it was snagged, one end of the wire was passed through an eye at the other end and the loop tightened around the aircraft until it was held securely.

The Tomcat was then carefully lifted clear of the sea floor and very slowly moved into shallow waters. There the divers were able to attach lifting slings for the final retrieval to the salvage recovery ship.

Nine years later again, on 23 June 1985, during flight AI182 from Toronto to Bombay, via Montreal and London, the Air India Boeing 747, VT-EFO Emperor Kanishka, exploded and crashed into the sea southwest of Ireland. It took with it all 329 persons on board, mostly Canadians of East Indian origin. Of the 307 passengers who were killed, 86 were children.

The aircraft suddenly disappeared from the radar screens at Shannon Air Traffic Control Centre at 08.13 BST, only minutes after receiving clearance to proceed to Heathrow. At the time of the incident it was flying at 965 kilometres per hour (600 miles per hour) at an altitude of 9,450 metres (31,000 feet).

The first reaction was for the authorities to treat the emergency as a routine Search and Rescue exercise and the Royal Air Force rescue base at Plymouth, Devon, immediately alerted Nimrod reconnaissance aircraft from RAF Kinloss and Sea King helicopters from RAF Brawdy and the Royal Navy Air Station at Culdrose. It very soon became apparent that this was futile, however, for all the signs were of a case of massive destruction. The extent and nature of the floating débris and the many bodies found in the water indicated a disaster of such horrific proportions that no-one could possibly have survived.

Ships too were directed to the scene, the first to arrive being the container ship *Laurentian Forrest*. With Irish Navy and Royal Navy vessels, which also arrived at the disaster site, they assisted with the recovery of bodies.

The wreckage was spread over a surface area of more than 42.5 square kilometres (20 square nautical miles) located approximately 215 kilometres (100 miles) south west of Ireland. This area was promptly marked with yellow and green sea dye and orange flares to assist with its location pending the placement of more permanent sea marks.

Sabotage was immediately suspected as the cause of the disaster, for a number of political and religious conflicts involving India seemed to provide a potential stimulus for such an extremist outrage - the dispute over the Kashmir with Pakistan, the Indian Government's involvement in the Tamil civil war in Sri Lanka and, of course the intense hostilities between the Sikh and Hindu communities which had already claimed as a victim, Mrs Indira Gandhi, the Indian Prime Minister.

Investigations into the incident were immediately initiated in a bid to determine the precise cause of the disaster and whether it had definitely resulted from a criminal act. The Indian Government set up its own inquiry because the aircraft had been operated by the national air carrier and the entire crew were Indian citizens. The Canadian Government, through the Canadian Aviation Safety Board, did likewise because all the passenger victims had been Canadian nationals. Interest in the Air India disaster was truly international for, besides the Indians and Canadians, the United States, as the aircraft's registration authority, Great Britain, France and Eire all became involved in the enquiries into the crash.

Critical to the investigations was the evidence that could be obtained from the aircraft's flight data recorder and cockpit voice recorder. While there was no guarantee that these instruments would provide conclusive proof of sabotage, it was nevertheless felt that they could give vital clues which, in conjunction with other enquiries, might suggest terrorist involvement and, if so, permit the perpetrators to be identified and apprehended. Certainly, a firm explanation of the crash's cause would be difficult to reach if the body of the aircraft along with its black boxes was not found.

The Irish Navy vessels *Aisling* and *Emer* and the Royal Navy ship HMS *Challenger* were despatched to the scene to attempt to pinpoint the flight instruments which had immediately commenced sending signals from their emergency locator transmitters (ELTs). In addition, the British

(far left) ; The developed CURV-III craft seen being lowered into the sea.
US Navy

(left): The SCARAB craft used in the salvage of the Air India jumbo's flight recorders.
Transpacific Communications

Department of Transport, at the request of the Indian Government, chartered the survey ship *Gardline Locator*, which carried sophisticated electronic equipment and its own mini submarine, to assist with the search. Normally based in the North Sea, she sailed from Great Yarmouth carrying DoT Accident Investigation Bureau inspectors on Friday, 28 June.

Although the wreckage and transponder signals indicated the general area for immediate search, it was impossible to know whether the critical stern and cockpit sections of the aircraft, which housed the recorders, had fallen into the sea elsewhere or even how the submerged parts of the wreckage had settled onto the sea-bed. Equally, it was not known whether the recorders were still attached to pieces of the wreckage or lying on their own. For this reason, the overall search area was initially established as 65 by 50 kilometres (approximately 40 by 30 miles), centred on the point where wreckage was most concentrated.

Already, the tracing signals were becoming fainter and the depth and the thermoclyne, the changes to the transmission properties of water due to temperature variation, were making them even weaker.

In order to narrow down the search area, the investigators first towed a hydrophone, an underwater listening device, through the water tuned to the ELT signals. Next, a deep sea sonar device was used to trace a "shadow" of the wreckage. From the results of these efforts, carried out by HMS *Challenger* and the *Gardline Locator*, the search team was able to determine the zone on which the subsequent, more intensive

phases of the exercise should be concentrated, a significantly reduced area of the ocean.

Progress at this point was hampered by the lack of availability of highly specialised equipment without which location and recovery could not be successfully accomplished. As Commander Frank Di George, the United States Navy salvage consultant attached to the recovery operation, put it, "No one had ever wanted to recover things from such a depth before". This was not strictly true, as revealed by the account of the project 'Jennifer' in Chapter 7 of this book, but such equipment was not readily at hand for commercial operators.

It was estimated that the recorders were lying at a depth of 1,650 or more metres (5,400 feet). The equipment regularly used for underwater work in the North Sea oil fields would have been quite easy to obtain but was of little value as it had been specifically designed for use only down to depths of a maximum of 915 metres (3,000 feet).

To commission and assemble at the site the types of equipment that were needed for this unique operation was going to take considerable time, the one commodity that the recovery team did not have in abundant quantities. In a vain bid to try to introduce a short cut to the proceedings, the Royal Navy's nuclear submarine HMS *Churchill*, which was in the vicinity, was invited to sweep the zone with her sophisticated submarine tracking sonars but this was to no avail. Although the signals could be picked up, their source could not be pinpointed.

Luckily, the ELTs had continued emitting signals long after the anticipated duration of their battery packs, faint though they were. When the French diesel electric cable layer *Leon Thevenin* arrived on the scene in early July, to relieve HMS *Challenger*, her rather more sophisticated sensory equipment was able to pick up positively the diminishing signal. The facility used to pick up the faint homing blip was a deep water passive receiver dragged along the sea-bed on a 5,250 metre (17,200 feet) umbilical lead behind the ship. For so long as she could maintain this contact, there was still hope.

Having been pinpointed, the signal position was charted, at the surface, to within a few feet and marked with transponders in readiness for the recovery team to take over. The *Thevenin* had brought with her, for the recovery phase, another robot submarine to replace the one operated by the *Gardline Locator* as this lacked the means of detecting the much reduced signals from the recorders. This new submersible was the SCARAB (Submerged Craft Assisting Repair And Burial), owned by Transpacific Communications Incorporated, which was also fitted with a television camera and a remote control arm.

Within hours, the team of recovery experts had successfully accomplished the first of its two objectives. After a six hour operation, the cockpit voice recorder from the Air India Boeing was brought to the surface by members of the team aboard the *Leon Thevenin*. Located and

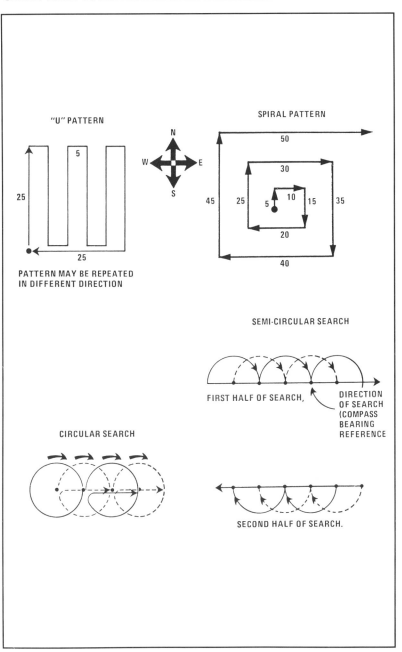

"U" PATTERN

SPIRAL PATTERN

5

25

25

PATTERN MAY BE REPEATED
IN DIFFERENT DIRECTION

N

W   E

S

50

30

45   25   5   10   15   35

20

40

SEMI-CIRCULAR SEARCH

135

FIRST HALF OF SEARCH,   DIRECTION
OF SEARCH
(COMPASS
BEARING
REFERENCE

CIRCULAR SEARCH

SECOND HALF OF SEARCH.

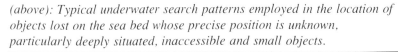

*(above): Typical underwater search patterns employed in the location of
objects lost on the sea bed whose precise position is unknown,
particularly deeply situated, inaccessible and small objects.*

*(below): The
Air India
jumbo jet*
Emperor
Kanishka
*which
crashed into
the sea west
of Ireland on
23 June 1985.*
Air India

136

recovered using the SCARAB submersible, the device was hauled onto the French ship's deck during the morning of 10 July. On the following day, the performance was repeated when the flight data recorder was retrieved in the same fashion from more than 1,825 metres (6,000 feet) down in the Atlantic. Before the end of that day the *Leon Thevenin* was already heading for Cork with the recorders, along with some sizeable chunks of aircraft fuselage which were also recovered. From here they were flown to London (Heathrow) before transfer to Bombay for examination by the members of the official Indian inquiry.

The retrieval of the Air India jumbo's flight recorders was one of the most spectacular salvage operations ever undertaken, judged by any standards, but the measure of the achievement was largely obscured at the time by the focus of press and public attention on the incident itself which had led to them ending up in the cold depths of the North Atlantic in the first place.

In the event, their recovery did not contribute overmuch to the official inquiries. It was not possible, it seems, on the basis of the information that they provided in isolation, to conclude that a terrorist act had been responsible for the disaster. Ultimately, though, the Indian Government inquiry did decide just that, stating that a bomb placed aboard the aircraft had caused the explosion. But, as yet, no one has been charged with the crime.

The Canadian Government would not go that far, the main reason being the lack of physical evidence because much of the débris from the plane was strewn over a wide area in a deep section of the Atlantic. Nevertheless, in the search for facts and conclusive evidence, the Canadians have continued to investigate the crash. As late as August 1989, as part of the "on-going criminal investigation", the crash site was revisited by the chartered French-registered ship *Abeille Supporter*, carrying new and much more technologically advanced underwater equipment, developed by the Vancouver company Deep Water Services since 1985. One suspects that, ultimately, deep ocean salvage stands to benefit to a far greater extent from this than the cause of justice.

Disasters Offshore

The emergence of the offshore oil and gas exploration industry in the 1960s introduced a totally new dimension to marine salvage. The structures erected on the sea-bed for production and accommodation purposes are inherently vulnerable to accidents, through stress caused by the hostile environmental forces in which they exist, through collision and through explosion and fire arising from leaks of the volatile substances being extracted. The accompanying risk of widespread pollution has meant that the salvage companies have benefitted, if that is not an inappropriate term, through their association with the offshore industry with much business dealing both with problems of recovery and spillage containment. Quite apart from this it has also resulted in much routine towage and support work, a useful mainstay of income.

There are, in particular, two aspects of salvage work involving offshore structures which deserve special mention because of the exacting nature of the technical demands they make of the salvage team, difficulties that are not experienced in any other sphere of marine salvage.

Capping a blow-out on an oil well in a landfield presents a big enough challenge but, on a mountainous sea in storm force winds, the same task requires almost superhuman skills, especially as the positioning of essential equipment, to where it is needed, is so much more difficult.

And, where capsized or sunken structures are concerned, the complications for the salvage operation are legion because of the unique characteristics of rig construction. Unlike a conventional hull shape, in which the strength of the vessel is relatively evenly distributed throughout its body, the integrity of a rig is localised, built-in by its design and method of fabrication, rather like a bridge. If, as a result of an accident, a critical support or brace has been weakened, then the integrity of the entire rig becomes suspect and conventional salvage techniques may aggravate this condition. Further, the buoyancy, compartmentation and centre of gravity of an upturned rig, which is to be righted, are much less easy to calculate than for a normal, displacement body shape.

Often too, in emergencies on offshore platforms, evacuation cannot always be as expeditiously achieved as from a land production field. Consequently, and tragically, the complex problems already described are intensified when there is a need to locate and rescue trapped survivors or, as is more usually the case, remove the bodies of victims for return to their families.

138

(top): The accommodation rig Alexander L. Kielland *alongside the production rig* Albuskjell *before the fatal collapse of the leg D forward starboard. She capsized in the position 56°28'N, 03°07'E.* Phillips Petroleum

(above): Work on the Alexander L. Kielland *in progress during the first salvage attempt, Autumn 1980, showing the buoyancy pods at the end of two of the four remaining legs, each with its own integral propulsion unit. The rig is turned almost 90 degrees.* Associated Press

CHAPTER 11

The following accounts describe incidents in which the offshore salvage operations were beset with issues of technical complexity and inclement weather and, because respectively they were the worst offshore tragedies to date, all the pressures rapidly to provide some sort of relief for bereaved relatives.

On 27 March 1980, at around 1800 hours (Greenwich Mean Time), Wick Radio intercepted distress messages advising that the Norwegian accommodation platform *Alexander L. Kielland* was listing to 50 degrees and in danger of sinking due to failure of one of its five support legs. The weather was appalling at the time - the wind was gusting to 110 kilometres per hour (60 mph) and waves in the area were up to 7.6 metres (25 feet) in height. The cloud cover was below 30 metres (100 feet).

Soon afterwards the rig collapsed and turned upside down, the severed leg floating free, towards the Albuskjell oilfield, presenting, in itself, another, quite distinct hazard to shipping and other fixed structures in the vicinity. Many of the men who had been aboard the platform were either dead or missing and unaccounted for.

The *Alexander L. Kielland* was one of a pair of self-propelled, semi-submersible platforms built by the Compagnie Francaise d'Enterprises Metalliques for the Stavanger Drilling Company and chartered to Phillips Petroleum, an American oil corporation based in Oklahoma. The other was the *Henrik Ibsen*. The *Kielland* had been fitted out as a hotel for oil workers and had been connected, by a gangway, to the Edda production platform.

Over the next twenty four hours, as the rescue operation unfolded, the detailed picture gradually emerged as to the extent of casualties and the scale of the task confronting salvors in order to recover the damaged structure. As is so often the case at the height of an emergency, confused, misleading and unduly optimistic announcements were made regarding the numbers of victims. Preliminary figures suggested that, of 225 persons aboard the rig, 103 had survived while only 7 were known to be dead. The remainder, who were officially missing, were hopefully still alive awaiting rescue. These numbers were soon adjusted, however, inevitably revealing a far higher death toll and, more realistically, admitting that the prospects for survival for those yet to be located were not good. The definitive breakdown ultimately released by the rig's operators disclosed that only 89 had been rescued from 212 persons who had been aboard the *Kielland* and that 123 others were either dead or presumed to be dead. It was by far the worst offshore accident on record. The confusion over numbers was explained as having resulted from the fact that the accident had occurred during a shift change. Also, because workers had been evacuated, simultaneously, from the Edda platform they had been mixed up with those taken off the *Alexander L. Kielland*, scattered around all the adjacent rigs to which they had been taken.

Though it is strictly speaking outside the scope of this book, the

subsequent inquiry attributed the failure of the rig's leg, D forward starboard, to metal fatigue in the welding of certain bracing joints. This was exacerbated by a serious lack of natural stability, characteristic of this design, which was later demonstrated during ballasting trials with the sister rig *Henrik Ibsen* on 7 April, as a result of which it settled on the bottom, listing 20 degrees.

An interesting alternative cause of the disaster, as conjectured by an eminent offshore consultant engineer but disputed by the authorities, was sabotage. Trondheim-based Ole Østlund's theory was that the *Alexander L. Kielland* was being used as a staging post for drugs being smuggled from Britain to Norway. When payments or deliveries were not made as scheduled, international gangsters apparently detonated explosives on the leg that failed.

The inverted rig lay in position 56°28'N, 03°07'E, the only sign of the overturned structure being four round pods, the bases of the remaining support legs, that were penetrating the surface. The destroyer *Overijssel* was co-ordinating the efforts to search for survivors but 48 hours after the accident, the rescue operation was abandoned when it was accepted that the remaining 80 or so persons still on the missing list were trapped aboard the rig.

The living quarters were now suspended some 50 metres (164 feet) below the surface in a tangle of pipelines and other débris. It was considered to be fruitless and too dangerous to send divers into the metal accommodation section to search for bodies and that this should not be undertaken until after the rig had been righted, a decision that was to have a profound impact, as the salvage exercise unfolded, on all subsequent actions involving the *Alexander L. Kielland*.

Divers were sent below, instead, to inspect the rig, to examine its integrity and particularly to determine whether the accommodation block could endure a righting operation intact. An oil derrick which had been mounted on the top of the platform was thought to have ripped free during the violent movements as the force 10 winds hurled the rig over and to have fallen to the sea bottom. This needed to be confirmed or the precise situation, if different, established for if the derrick was still in place it could introduce serious problems when the rig was moved, if it snagged on the bottom. In principle, officials of Phillips Petroleum and representatives of the Norwegian Government had decided already to tow the capsized platform to Norway where it could be righted in the shelter of coastal waters.

Having effectively decided, in outline, the course of action to be taken, preparations were begun for the first stage of the operation, the 360 kilometre (300 mile) tow to a fjord near Stavanger. Operated from the diving support vessels *Seaway Eagle* and *Seaway Falcon*, the remote controlled submersible SCORPIO (Submersible Craft for Ocean Repair, Positioning, Inspection and Observation) was used to cut away all trailing

cables, pipelines and other projections from beneath the platform. It was decided that the drilling derrick, which had been discovered, incredibly, to be still attached, would be left in place because removal at sea would introduce an unacceptable delay. Work on cleaning up the *Alexander L. Kielland* commenced on 1 April with the tow due to begin on the weekend of 5-6 April, although, in the event, deteriorating weather and delays on clearing the underwater obstructions resulted in a postponement of seven days. Meanwhile, contracts were placed with all the companies whose craft or equipment was required for the towing operation so that everything would be standing by, ready for the commencement.

The tow would be via the British sector of the North Sea, across the Ekofisk-Teesside oil pipeline route, because water was deep enough here to allow clearance for the derrick. It was anticipated that the tow would take at least a week because Phillips Petroleum was concerned that the platform should be moved in such a way that any bodies trapped inside would not be dislodged and lost. Concern over the recovery of the bodies of the victims was already being given, perhaps rightly, though, (it must be said, untypically), a higher priority than salvage and restoration of the rig itself.

The precise route of the tow was southwest towards the Argyll field, then west and northwest to clear the Duncan, Auk and Fulmar fields before turning northeast towards Norway. On arriving off the coast of Norway, the tow was to proceed to Skudenesfjord, off the island of Kvitsoy, and later, after a brief rest period, to Tysvaer in Boknafjord.

The tow had three tugs forward, the lead vessel being the 499 GRT *Tender Power* owned by Wilhelmsen Offshore Services, and one on each side carrying the platform's anchors. Aft of the tow were two trawlers with a fishing net suspended between them. Stationed further ahead and behind the convoy were two ships, each equipped with sonar, while a diving support vessel was also in attendance. This great fleet of ships progressed at a snail-like 1.5 knots, finally arriving near East Bokn island, at the north side of Boknafjord, position 59°15'N, 05°33'E, in the early hours of 20 April 1980. The rig was lying in water 120 metres (394 feet) deep, secured to four anchors.

A second, intensive examination of the damaged *Alexander L. Kielland* was now authorised as a preliminary to deciding the rig's future. This study concluded that the damage to the structure was not so extensive that it could not be turned upright. Nevertheless, it was expected that the salvage technique to be employed would utilise a combination of ballast trimming and air cushions, precisely positioned according to computer calculations, and that no external, mechanical force of any kind would be applied since this might lead to further structural damage. Copies of the study of the rig's condition were issued to interested parties prior to requesting salvage tenders.

By early August, six tenders for the righting operation had been

141

received by the owners and the Norwegian insurance underwriters, three from Norwegian concerns and three from foreign companies. The rig was insured for approximately $60 million (£25 million). The righting and subsequent conversion of the *Alexander L. Kielland* to a production platform was estimated to cost around $34 million (£14 million). For as long as salvage was attainable, therefore, the insurers were not willing to declare the rig a constructive total loss. This stance was welcomed by the Norwegian Government which had most positively aligned itself with the aspirations of the mourning families who urgently wanted the bodies of their loved ones recovered. From this point, no alternative was ethically acceptable to the Norwegian people. The number of missing workmen had, by then, reduced to 79.

The salvage contract was awarded to a consortium of the Swedish concern Nicoverken Norge A/S and the British consulting engineering company SD Marine, a division of the Southampton-based Structural Dynamics Limited. As expected, salvage was to be effected by altering the wrecked rig's centre of gravity by controlled ballasting and the use of air bags. It was to be executed in Gandsfjorden, in the Stavanger harbour area, and towage from the rig's existing position to the new location, about 48 kilometres (30 miles) distant, was scheduled for the end of August 1980.

142

The British salvage tug *Salvageman* (1,599 GRT/1980), owned by United Towing, was contracted to undertake the tow, also to assist in anchor handling operations in conjunction with the Norwegian tugs *Normand Rough* and *Lunde Semor*.

Again, the weather intervened, even though it was high summer, and first the tow and then the salvage operation was delayed. It was not until nearly the end of October that the righting operation got underway, some seven months having already passed since the capsizing incident.

Pre-salvage preparations had necessitated the fitting of underwater valves and the strategic placement of 370 air bags. Once underway, the salvage operation initially made good progress - on 30 October the platform had turned by 3 degrees; by 6 November it had reached 66 degrees; on 11 November it had turned to just beyond 80 degrees. As the rotation proceeded, the air bags were progressively inflated to support the rig in its partly turned state. The most critical point in the operation would be reached when the platform had been turned by 85 to 95 degrees for it would then be on its side with the legs in a horizontal position. Movement beyond this stage, to an upright position, would depend exclusively on the lift applied through the process of inflation but this had to be increased in an extremely delicate manner for too sudden a push could give sufficient momentum to the rotating platform to cause it to overturn again.

Just as success was in prospect, with the rig turned as far as 115

degrees, serious buoyancy problems were encountered through a build-up of trapped air in the rig's stairwells and horizontal braces which began to affect the sensitive balancing manoeuvre.

An attempt was made to flood these areas or drive out the air with high pressure water jets to overcome the problem, but to no avail. Thus it was that temporarily (at least that was how it was announced at the time) the salvage operation was brought to a standstill as the options were reviewed. The salvors favoured supplementing the measures already employed by using sheerlegs, on top of piles, and high density ballast in a series of pontoon tanks to give extra support as the rig passed through the critical phase of the righting exercise.

The insurers expressed grave concern over the additional stress that the platform would be subjected to which might lead to it breaking up and sinking. The Norwegian Government was also anxious in case blockage of the shipping channels in the approaches to Stavanger harbour resulted from the loss of the rig. A period of prevarication ensued during which the salvors, owners and insurers haggled over what could and could not be done to expedite the recovery.

While the decision on what was to be done next was awaited, the rig was maintained at an angle of 76 degrees, at a cost of £50,000 per day. The flotation bags had only a limited life, however, and could not be maintained under pressure indefinitely. Therefore, on 2 December, in the absence of any directive and with no further progress made, it was decided to abandon this effort to salve the *Alexander L. Kielland*. The Swedish/British consortium withdrew and the insurers and owners were left to agree a total loss settlement.

Under normal circumstances, the whole affair would have been terminated at this point with the insurers arranging for the disposal of the rig by deliberate scuttling in order to contain further financial loss. But this did not take account of the commitment made by the Norwegian Government to the families of the victims assuring them that, by whatever means the bodies still trapped on the wreck would be recovered. In Norway, public unrest over the unduly protracted and fruitless salvage exercise was growing, with shipyard workers and other trades union groups threatening strike action if there was not a quick resolution to the whole matter.

Before the salvage of the rig could be advanced from this point, quite involved, political and financial complications had to be resolved first. Through settlement of the insurance claim, ownership of the *Alexander L. Kielland* had passed from Stavanger Drilling to the Norwegian Oil Risk Insurance Pool, the underwriters. The Pool was unwilling to sanction a second bid to salve the rig unless the Norwegian Government first agreed to guarantee the operation against failure or, if it was successful, against any other financial losses incurred. The Pool's concern was that a great deal of money could be invested in attempting to

turn the rig only to be lost if the bid failed. Equally, in the event that it succeeded, they could still be left facing massive losses if the resale value of the *Alexander L. Kielland* was less than the cost of recovering it. As the pledge to the victims' families was not made by the Pool it considered the onus for funding a second salvage bid rested with the Government. The Government, for its part, was only willing to guarantee the costs of the uprighting operation but no other cost penalties sustained from this point because its only concern was the recovery of the bodies. By this time, March 1981, 35 bodies remained unaccounted for, presumably still trapped in the upturned structure.

The Norwegian Oil Risk Insurance Pool would not accept the limitations to the protection being offered and refused to proceed on this basis. The Government would not agree to increase its offer of an 80% guarantee, resulting in stalemate. In an attempt to break the impasse and apply political pressure on the Government, the Pool offered to transfer temporarily ownership of the rig. Under this arrangement, the responsibility and cost of the recovery operation would pass to the Government and then, following its completion, the *Alexander L. Kielland* would revert to its owners for disposal, on the face of it a reasonable solution to the problem.

Nevertheless, in spite of this offer and the Government's declared determination fully to relieve the gnawing anxiety that afflicted the families of the rig victims remaining unaccounted for, the controversy dragged on, unresolved, for the next eighteen months. During this time an election in Norway returned a changed Government, complicating matters further, for the new administration was not party to the recovery pledge and did not feel morally bound to fulfil it.

Meanwhile, to complicate matters more, the leading salvage organisation Neptun and the classification body Det norske Veritas publicly registered their views on the viability and achievability of salvage, following their examination and evaluation of the rig's state. Neptun thought salvage was possible, Det norske Veritas considered it was not, adding that, in their opinion, it was also potentially dangerous to those who would be involved. They recommended instead that the rig should be scuttled without any additional attempt at salvage. None of this particularly helped the protracted negotiations between the Insurance Pool and the Government, each of which was already paranoiac about, respectively, the financial liabilities or the dangers of creating an unnecessary navigational hazard.

Finally, in August 1982, the deadlock was broken by a compromise agreement. The Norwegian Parliament, the Storting, conceded improvement of the Government guarantees to a limit of 90% while the underwriters agreed that, if the rig was successfully salved and proved to have some value, the money so derived would go towards the cost of the salvage, now estimated to cost $25 million.

Preparatory engineering work and a feasibility study for the second salvage bid was contracted to Norway's Stolt-Nielsen Seaway Contracting. The contract included the preparation of calculations, drawings, specifications and schedules - virtually a blueprint for the uprighting operation. Indeed, this formed the basis of the technical specification issued to companies interested in bidding for the salvage contract.

Prospective bidders were invited to consider either of two options for providing the additional buoyancy as the rig was righted. These were to weld the platform's fifth leg back into place or to build large flotation tanks which would be attached to each of the other four legs. As it turned out the latter alternative was settled on by all of the five shortlisted bidders: Smit Tak International and Wijsmuller BV, from the Netherlands, Neptun AB from Sweden, Stolt-Nielsen and Brodrene Sorensen, which are both Norwegian companies.

Eight more months had passed while the requests for tenders were issued, the responses analysed, the bidders shortlisted and the negotiations concluded until, on 7 April 1983, the contract for the second salvage attempt was awarded to Stolt-Nielsen Seaway Contracting. The Norwegian Government also engaged Kvaerner Engineering as consultant specialist advisers. The order for fabricating the four supplementary buoyancy units went to Bergens Mekanica Verksted and work began on them immediately. Once in place, the righting operation could commence. During July 1983, in readiness for the righting operation, the upturned rig was moved, for the third time, a short distance to a new location nearer to shore but where the water depth was not significantly shallower.

145

Stolt-Nielsen's plan for the second salvage bid involved pumping air into the huge containers welded to the remaining legs while, simultaneously, the water within the rig structure was pumped out. Powerful skid chains, operated by land-based winches, would be attached to two of the legs to pull in one direction while two tugs, connected by chains to the other legs, would pull in the the other direction to keep the rig in balance as the lifting process proceeded. The main concern in using this method was that the weight of water in the main accommodation modules, if undrained and unsupported, might cause them to be torn from the structure.

The trimming operation finally got underway on 7 September 1983 with a target for completion of 15 September because shortly thereafter the seasonal North Sea storms were expected to set in.

In effect the operation was to be undertaken in a number of stages (rotation to 40, 90, 105, 120 and 175 degree positions) with pauses between each to assess progress and ensure that successive stages would proceed according to plan. Yet again problems were encountered, causing the operation to fall behind programme, first through the weather

* See
photograph on
page 157

deteriorating sooner than anticipated and then through a ballasting problem. A number of hoses which passed through deep water were affected by the great pressure at that depth so that air could not be pumped out through them. After a remote-controlled mini-submarine was sent down to sever the hoses, it was possible for the trimming procedure to be resumed.

As an interesting aside, it was necessary, as part of this emergency corrective action, to have a diver breach a 70 metre (230 feet) safety zone surrounding the platform. Special permission for this had to be sought from the Government's Trade and Shipping Minister.

On 16 September, only one day beyond the projected deadline, Stolt-Nielsen was able to announce that the righting operation had been successfully concluded. The platform had been turned through 178 degrees and the salvors were preparing to stabilise it prior to moving it to a deep water anchorage for inspection and removal of the bodies still believed to be trapped inside 3 years after the disaster occured.

The harrowing scenes that followed require no description here. Suffice it to say that the Norwegian Government's objective of fulfilling its obligation to victims' families was realised. On reflection it is hard to avoid drawing the conclusion that, having made this commitment, much misery might have been spared had the Government not haggled at such length over the financial burden of discharging this pledge.

Weeks later, on 2 November, following a thorough inspection of the decks and superstructure by the police, the official inquiry commission and representatives of interested parties, the platform was returned to its owners, the Norwegian Oil Risk Insurance Pool, for disposal. The Pool proceeded to do what, in any other situation, lit would have done in the first place - the platform was blown up and sunk it. Towed to Nedstrandsfjord, north of Stavanger, the *Alexander L. Kielland* was finally scuttled on 18 November 1983, in 700 metres (2,500 feet) of water. It ended one of the most bizarre salvage episodes ever as the experiences of 44 nerve-racking months were buried, with the rig, in a watery grave.

Just under five years later, on 6 July 1988, another disaster occurred in the North Sea of a magnitude that even overshadowed the awfulness of the *Alexander L. Kielland* catastrophe. At 20.58 (Greenwich Mean Time) on that fateful night, Occidental Petroleum's *Piper Alpha* rig, situated approximately 220 kilometres (120 miles) northeast of Aberdeen, in position 58° 28'N, 00° 15'E suffered a series of massive explosions followed by the most terrible conflagration.

Luckily, a naval task force, engaged in a NATO exercise, was in the vicinity and was able to render assistance. Even so, the loss of life was immense, resulting in the tragedy being the worst ever to be suffered by the offshore oil industry.

The first explosion was later attributed to a gas escape from module

C, the gas compression module, which was located, unfortunately, almost directly beneath the rig's accommodation module. The damage caused by this explosion triggered a chain of events which led to the almost total destruction of *Piper Alpha*. Diesel fuel, contained in tanks above modules B and C, was ignited, adding to the intensity of the already-raging fire and setting off further explosions. One of these ruptured the gas pipeline from the Tartan field, producing a massive fireball that totally devastated the crippled platform, splitting it from top to bottom. At the height of the fire, the flames were at least 105 metres (345 feet) high and clearly visible from a distance of 95 kilometres (60 miles).

All that remained afterwards was a fraction of the original structure. Two flarestacks atop the blackened and contorted skeleton were still belching thick smoke into the sky and at the sides crazily-canted cranes projected out over the sea as if in broken deference to the terrible forces that had been unleashed in destruction of the rig.

The *Piper* platform was situated at the heart of a cluster of six production fields supplying gas and oil to the United Kingdom mainland. Up to 560,000 barrels of oil were exported every day from the Piper, Tartan, Claymore, Highlander, Scapa and Petronella fields via a complex of pipelines to the Flotta terminal in the Orkney Islands. Gas was exported via a trunk line to Total Oil's MCP-01 platform midway along the Frigg-St Fergus pipeline. The devastation of *Piper Alpha* had catastrophic consequences, bringing all production in the area to a standstill. It is a measure of the dimension of the *Piper Alpha* disaster, as it affected the offshore oil industry generally, that it caused a 12% reduction of the United Kingdom's daily oil production of 2.4 million barrels which ironically had the effect in turn of boosting the flagging price of oil by $1.10 per barrel from its previous price of $14.00.

There was great confusion over the extent of casualties; just the same as had happened with the earlier *Alexander L. Kielland* disaster, with different figures were issued by the Grampian Police, Occidental and H.M. Coastguard. At first, the number of persons aboard the platform was put at 227 with 73 rescued, 153 unaccounted for and 1 corroborated death. Later, after the search for survivors was finally abandoned at 22.50 GMT on 8 July, these figures were amended to 64 confirmed survivors and 166 dead. The casualties ranged from men who were able to walk away to those seriously injured with 50% burns. Only 18 bodies had been recovered. The bodies of the remaining 148 who were missing were presumed to be still aboard the wrecked platform.

The tragedy was compounded when two persons from a rescue craft from the motor supply vessel *Sandhaven* were lost during the search operation, raising the casualty toll to 168.

In the case of the *Alexander L. Kielland*, salvage was initiated primarily to recover the bodies of victims although there was also a real interest in retrieving and restoring the platform itself. The situation was

147

rather different where the *Piper Alpha* was concerned. The rig had been so severely ravaged that there were genuine doubts as to whether any recognisable human remains could be found. Nevertheless, the rig's operators determined that every effort would be made, in response to the very natural desires of the next of kin, to recover bodies but an equal, if not higher, priority was given in these circumstances to other vital matters - dealing with the pollution caused by leaking oil and restoring production to the other unaffected fields.

Successful accomplishment of all three of the salvage objectives depended first on extinguishing the fires still burning on the *Piper Alpha* and cooling the structure, capping the leaking wellheads and stemming the flow of combustible fuel that was feeding the inferno. Until the latter task, in particular, was fully achieved the risk of more explosions could not be discounted. Only one man was capable of implementing the actions appropriate to dealing with this situation, the leader of the team of internationally-renowned specialists in oilwell blow-out capping and firefighting, Houston-based Paul 'Red' Adair.

By late on 8 July, having been engaged by Occidental Petroleum to apply his special skills to dealing with the *Piper Alpha* predicament he was already heading for the wreck to evaluate the circumstances. Early on the following day, Adair and members of his team were lowered onto the smouldering hulk of the rig in a metal basket attached to a crane from the firefighting and support vessel *Tharos* which was already on the scene rendering assistance.

The party spent an hour on the platform and, later, scrutinised video film taken by an unmanned ROV (Remote Observation Vehicle) submarine circling underwater beneath the damaged installation. Afterwards, 'Red' Adair was able to give his assessment and outline the plan of action for making the platform safe.

Fires were still burning on a number of *Piper Alpha*'s 36 wellheads and scattered, loose metal débris in the welldeck area was blocking access to the leaking gas and oil outlets. This would have to be cleared before any moves to cap the wells could be made. Capping the fractured wells from aboard the platform was the preferred option but, as a contingency, should this fail or prove to be difficult, work would commence on drilling a directional relief well. The purpose of such a relief well is to make contact with the bottom of the well which is blowing out, to intercept it at this point and, by injecting water and drilling mud, to staunch the flow of oil feeding the fires on the surface.

There are a number of methods of extinguishing well fires. The basic method proposed by 'Red' Adair in this case is known as "bullheading". It involves fitting new valves and pipe manifolds on the top of each of the blown wells. Water has to be sprayed on the flames while the system is fitted and a high-pressure hose inserted in the top of the well. Sea water, mixed with chemicals to make it heavier, is then

(left): Fire-fighting in progress, the MSV Tharos *close in with her water jets spraying the flames aboard the* Piper Alpha. Occidental Oil.

(below): The Piper Alpha *rig in perspective view showing the key features.*

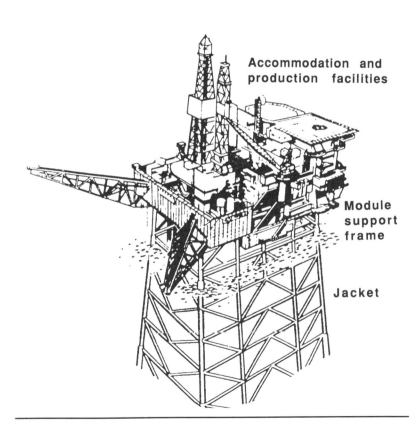

Accommodation and production facilities

Module support frame

Jacket

149

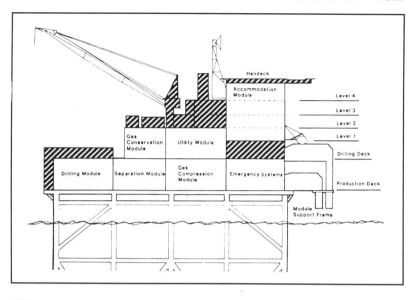

(top): Cross section of the Piper Alpha *rig showing the deck levels and the location of the Gas Compression Module relative to the Accommodation Module*

(above): The remains of the Piper Alpha *platform after the fire had been suppressed. Overhead a Coastguard S61-N helicopter on charter from Bristow Helicopters.* Occidental Oil

pumped down the well to force open the down-hole safety valve, which has invariably slammed shut during the blow-out, to push the escaping oil back into its reservoir. The next move is to kill the well completely by plugging it with cement.

Another, more-sophisticated technique, is known as "snubbing". This requires the removal of the blow-out preventer or "Christmas Tree", as it is known, an arrangement of valves and flanges for controlling pressure, and hydraulically forcing a new drill pipe down the well hole. This provides a new circulation path for escaping hydro-carbons, permitting them to travel up the inside of the pipe to be diverted to one side of the wellhead where they can be safely ignited and burnt off. A return to normal production may then be possible if pressure in the well can be gradually reduced.

Other methods of fighting well fires and capping blow-outs include the fitting of a steel sleeve around the well casing into which liquid nitrogen is passed to form an ice plug or, in conjunction with drilling a relief well, "crimping" a well by physically squeezing the top shut. Directional relief wells alone can also be employed as a fire quenching technique. The biggest problem for directional relief well drillers is locating precisely, beneath the sea-bed, the blown-out well. The directional relief well is drilled at an angle and magnetic sensory devices, inserted down the well hole, are used to detect the steel casing of the targeted well.

151

Back on the scene of the *Piper Alpha* blow-out, the authorities had declared a danger zone around the damaged rig to keep unauthorised shipping and aircraft out of the area and permit uninterrupted, hazard-free movement of equipment, as necessary, in the vicinity of the rig.

This had a radius of 18.5 kilometres (10 nautical miles) and extended upwards to a height of 1,220 metres (4,000 feet).

Adair's team set to work straight away but almost immediately ran into difficulties as the weather deteriorated. Winds approaching 75 kilometres an hour (45 mph), whipping up the seas, fanned the fires still flaring from the leaking wells. Over the next few days attempts to cap them had to be repeatedly postponed and it was only possible to continue débris clearance during brief interludes. Meanwhile, the *Tharos* continued to douse the scorched and damaged structure, assisted by the support and supply vessels, *Maersk Cutter*, *Maersk Logger* and *V.S.O. Performer*.

By 14 July the semi-submersible mobile drilling platform *Kingsnorth UK*, which had been allocated to the task of drilling a directional relief well to *Piper* well P1, was in position 1,000 metres (3,280 feet) east of *Piper Alpha* in readiness to commence work. The specialist firm Eastman Christensen supervised this operation which involved boring up to 2,590 metres (8,500 feet) under the sea-bed. Twenty four hours later, a second mobile drilling platform, the *Ocean Ben Loyal*, was positioned some 1,500 metres (4,920 feet) to the west of *Piper*

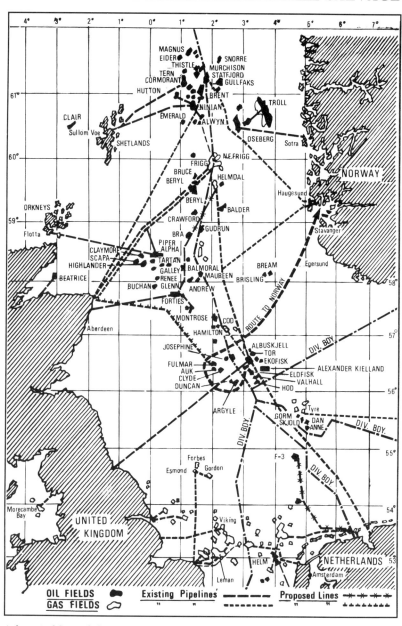

(above): Map of the North Sea showing the positions of the rigs
Alexander L. Kielland *and* Piper Alpha, *at the time of their respective
accidents, with the general complex of oil and gas production fields. The
dotted line indicates the route taken when the* Alexander L. Kielland *was
towed to Norway.*

Alpha, to stand by in case a second relief well was required.

The other *Piper* wells that were burning and needed to be capped were P3, P21, P31, P47, and P53 but, in order to make the structure fully safe, 'Red' Adair intended to plug all 36 of the rig's wells with cement. Before this could be done, it would be necessary to change all the valves from each wellhead, an operation which, it was estimated, would take at least two weeks to complete.

Through late July into August 1988, the programme of stabilising the blown-out wells proceeded slowly but surely, delayed only by constant interruptions as the teams of workmen battled with intermittently adverse weather conditions.

By 19 July, well P47 had been successfully killed. Two days later it had been safely blocked with cement. The same day, the *Kingsnorth UK* reached a depth of 1,070 metres (3,510 feet) as the drilling operation on the relief well progressed satisfactorily. The pollution situation remained unchanged with a continuing light spillage into the sea but the slick was being broken up by the natural action of the heavy seas. A number of isolated bodies had also been found by this time reducing the number of men unaccounted for to 137.

Twelve days later, on 31 July, 'Red' Adair was able to announce that all fires were out and that all *Piper Alpha*'s wells were stable. The *Kingsnorth UK* had breached well P1 at a depth of 1,790 metres (5,870 feet) and, after sealing the well, had terminated work and was preparing to move from the scene after its anchors were pulled. Wells P3, P47, and P53 had also been plugged with cement while wells P21 and P31 were being controlled with seawater prior to cementing. From this point, the pollution problem improved dramatically although it was agreed that a pollution control vessel should remain on location until the cement plugging operation on the platform was complete.

On 4 August, 16 wells had had their first cement plug installed; by the next day the number had increased to 21 and by 6 August it was 25. Progress slowed after that but still, by the end of August, work on 32 of the platform's 36 wells had been completed. By this time, too, subsea inspection of the platform's jacket had also resumed.

In order fully to restore production and export of oil from the surrounding fields that had been affected by the *Piper Alpha* disaster it had been agreed with the Department of Energy that the T-junction of the Claymore and Piper to Flotta pipelines should be permanently removed and a new bypass link established to reconnect the Claymore and Tartan fields with the mainland, permitting oil to be sent direct. This work was also in hand by early September 1988 and it was expected that production would be able to recommence in the last quarter of 1988.

On 5 September, Occidental made the announcement that had been earnestly awaited, that all 36 *Piper Alpha* wells had been made secure. As the various support vessels engaged in the stabilisation operation

153

began to leave the scene, a team of saturation divers continued with the undersea inspection of the rig operating out of a three-man diving bell from the *Seaway Condor* in eight hour shifts. Their task was to remove débris and eliminate hazards from around the rig before divers could undertake a search of the sea-bed for missing men.

Two of *Piper Alpha's* three main accommodation sections were discovered intact in the underwater wreckage during the course of this work. That this was where the missing victims were located was beyond doubt and preparations were therefore begun for lifting the sections on to a crane barge where they could be inspected in relative safety. Clamps and brackets were fitted to each of the modules in readiness for the lift which was scheduled to take place over two days 17-18 September. The last accommodation module was finally raised on 15 October 1988.

Once they had been removed and following a thorough search to account for all the remaining bodies still missing, the rig's remains were demolished. Having obtained Government approval, Occidental proceeded to clear the disaster site by a controlled explosion which toppled the top 75 metres (246 feet) of the *Piper Alpha* skeleton while it was still substantially intact.

So it was that by the end of October, less than four months after the tragic incident had occurred, all bodies had been recovered, the damaged rig had been safely demolished, the adjacent oil fields had been reconnected to Flotta, permitting output to be resumed, and all redundant pipework in the area around *Piper Alpha* had been dredged up and removed. It is not intended that this expeditiously achieved salvage operation should be compared with the much more protracted efforts to right the *Alexander L. Kielland* where quite different, less easily overcome problems were encountered. Facilitation of the *Piper Alpha* salvage owed itself to the early involvement of specialist "wild-well" firefighters.

Even though they may employ staff with some experience of well fires, when serious difficulties are encountered most oil companies turn immediately to the likes of Paul 'Red' Adair or any of the new generation of blow-out specialists, typified by Neal Adams and John Wright. These individuals travel, often at a moment's notice, from one fire or blow-out to the next - from the North Sea to Texas, from offshore in the Gulf of Mexico to onshore in the Soviet Union. They are as famous, deservedly, in their own right as any of the big salvage companies, making a proportionately greater and more effective contribution to salvage work in individual human terms than any other persons engaged in the salvage industry.

BIBLIOGRAPHY/ DATA SOURCES

Books, Reports etc.

Ardman, Harvey   "*Normandie*, Her Life and Times"
                               (Franklin Watts, 1985)

Ballard, Dr.Richard   "The Discovery of the *Titanic*"
                               (Hodder & Stoughton, 1987)

Birkenhead, Captain P. (salvage surveyor)
                               "A Brief Resumé of the Wreck
                               Removal Operation of the M.T.
                               Betelgeuse"

Braynard, Frank   "Lives of the Liners"
                               (Cornell Maritime Press, 1947)

Goold-Adams, Richard   "The Return of the *Great Britain*"
                               (Weidenfeld & Nicolson, 1976)

Hatcher, Michael and Thornycroft, Anthony
                               "The Nanking Cargo"
                               (Hamish Hamilton, 1987)

Joint Nautical Archaeology Policy Committee
                               "Heritage at Sea"
                               (National Maritime Museum, 1989)

Lewis, Flora   "One of Our H-Bombs is Missing"
                               (Bantam Books, 1967)

Lloyds Weekly CasualtyRecords (Lloyds of London Press
                               and Guildhall Library, London)

Maxtone-Graham, John   "The North Atlantic Run"
                               (Cassell, 1972)

155

NASA Facts · "Space Shuttle Mission Summary 1984, STS Missions 41-B thru 51-A"

NASA Information Summaries

"Long Duration Exposure Facility (LDEF)"

NASA Press Kits · "Space Shuttle Mission STS 51-A, November 1984"
"Space Shuttle Mission STS 32, December 1989"

Naval Historical Branch, Ministry of Defence
"HMS *Edinburgh* - Summary of Service 1939-1942"

Smit International · "The Involvement of Smit Tak International Bergingsbedrijf BV in one of the Greatest Wreck Removal Operations Ever Performed"

156 · United States Navy Bureau of Ships Records Group 19
"Records on the salvage of the USS *Lafayette* (AP-53, redesignated APV-4) and the recovery and reconstruction of the USS *Wakefield* (AP-21)" (United States National Archives, Washington, DC)

Vallintine, Reg · "Divers and Diving" (Blandford Press, 1981)

Winchester, Clarence (Editor)

"Shipping Wonders of the World" (ca 1939)

Journals and Newspapers

"Boston Globe" · - 1/10/1942 to 10/2/1944

"Diver" · - magazine of the British Sub-Aqua Club

"Halifax Herald" · - 3/9/1942 to 4/10/1942

BIBLIOGRAPHY

"Lloyds List"

"Marine News"

"New Scientist"   - 8/8/1985, article on passenger
                                ferry accidents and safety matters

"Parade" (USA)   - 11/5/1975, article on Project Jennifer

"Portsmouth News"

"Safety at Sea"

"Southern Evening Echo"

"Subnotes"   - 1/1987, article on Operation E,
                                the salvage of gold from HMS
                                Edinburgh
"The Times"

"Tug"   - house magazine of Smit
                                International, number 45/1987,
                                article on the *Herald of Free
                                Enterprise* salvage

"Veritas Forum"   - corporate magazine of Det norske
                                Veritas

*(below left):
The second bid
to right the
Alexander L.
Kielland
underway in
1983.
Ultimately, it
proved to be
successful.
Here the
platform has
been turned
through 145
degrees. The
living quarters
can be seen at
the centre.*
Associated
Press

Index

INDEX